PRENTICE HALL

MIDDLE GRADES
MATH
TOOLS FOR SUCCESS

CASTILLERO

Practice Workbook

Course 1

PRENTICE HALL
Simon & Schuster Education Group
A VIACOM COMPANY

ISBN: 0-13-428483-6

Printed in the United States of America.

2 3 4 5 6 7 8 9   01 00 99 98 97

Table of Contents

PRACTICE WORKSHEETS

CUMULATIVE REVIEWS **Page**

Inventory of Basic Skills

Show all your work on a separate sheet of paper.

Skill 1 Ordering numbers

Write the following in order from least to greatest.

1. 4,251 6,019 1,987   **2.** 597 795 957 579   **3.** 716 2,086 397 3,624

Skill 2 Using Place Value

Write the place value of each underlined digit.

4. 46,019   **5.** 9,643   **6.** 108,468   **7.** 63,914

Skill 3 Adding Whole Numbers

Add the following.

8.	**9.**	**10.**	**11.**
37	28	73,207	8,603
70	196	54,691	48
86	5	+ 30,426	23,915
+ 49	+ 407		+ 642

Skill 4 Subtracting Whole Numbers

Subtract the following.

12.	**13.**	**14.**	**15.**
69,865	8,372	9,053	8,000
− 7,103	− 2,536	− 4,178	− 3,496

Skill 5 Multiplying Whole Numbers

Multiply the following.

16.	**17.**	**18.**	**19.**
4,375	783	609	418
× 6	× 46	× 73	× 257

Skill 6 Dividing Whole Numbers

Divide the following.

20. $6\overline{)1,962}$ **21.** $7\overline{)9,632}$ **22.** $19\overline{)8,797}$ **23.** $32\overline{)2,272}$

Skill 7 Adding Fractions and Mixed Numbers

Add the following. Write each answer in simplest form.

24. $\frac{7}{12} + \frac{4}{12}$ **25.** $\frac{1}{8} + \frac{5}{8}$ **26.** $3\frac{4}{10} + 6\frac{3}{10}$ **27.** $8\frac{3}{15} + 5\frac{7}{15}$

Inventory of Basic Skills (continued)

Skill 8 Subtracting Fractions and Mixed Numbers

Subtract. Write each answer in simplest form.

28. $\frac{7}{9} - \frac{2}{9}$ 29. $\frac{11}{12} - \frac{5}{12}$ 30. $9\frac{6}{7} - 2\frac{1}{7}$ 31. $10\frac{5}{6} - 3\frac{3}{6}$

Skill 9 Multiplying Fractions and Mixed Numbers

Multiply. Write each answer in simplest form.

32. $\frac{1}{3} \times \frac{5}{6}$ 33. $\frac{2}{3} \times \frac{1}{4}$ 34. $6 \times \frac{3}{4}$ 35. $1\frac{3}{4} \times \frac{1}{2}$

Skill 10 Dividing Fractions and Mixed Numbers

Divide. Write each answer in simplest form.

36. $\frac{1}{3} \div \frac{4}{5}$ 37. $\frac{2}{5} \div \frac{1}{10}$ 38. $3 \div \frac{1}{4}$ 39. $2\frac{1}{3} \div \frac{5}{6}$

Skill 11 Adding Decimals

Add the following.

40. $2.6 + 3.5 + 7.8$ 41. $0.46 + 0.92 + 0.75$

42. $45.96 + 2.7 + 0.032$ 43. $2.39 + 41.6 + 0.5$

Skill 12 Subtracting Decimals

Subtract the following.

44. $36.8 - 21.4$ 45. $978.6 - 43.9$

46. $25.968 - 6.7$ 47. $8 - 1.7$

Skill 13 Multiplying Decimals

Multiply the following.

48. 2.6×1.8 49. 0.51×3.2

50. 37.5×0.17 51. 31×0.24

Skill 14 Dividing Decimals

Divide the following.

52. $6 \overline{)25.38}$ 53. $4 \overline{)0.864}$ 54. $0.3 \overline{)2.613}$ 55. $0.18 \overline{)0.414}$

Beginning of Year Self-Assessment Survey

Directions: This self-assessment can help you think about yourself, what you like, and what you can do in math. Answer each question as honestly as possible.

1. Here is a list of skills. Check each one that you have learned.

☐ add whole numbers   ☐ find common factors
☐ subtract whole numbers   ☐ compare fractions
☐ multiply whole numbers   ☐ add fractions
☐ divide whole numbers   ☐ subtract fractions
☐ find factors   ☐ multiply fractions
☐ write decimals   ☐ divide fractions
☐ add decimals   ☐ use ratios
☐ subtract decimals   ☐ use percents
☐ multiply decimals   ☐ make graphs
☐ divide decimals   ☐ make frequency tables
☐ find number patterns   ☐ make predictions
☐ estimate answers   ☐ use formulas
☐ find perimeter and area of polygons   ☐ make coordinate graphs
☐ find circumference and area of circles ☐ solve word problems
☐ measure angles

2. Which skills are fairly easy for you to do?

   _____

   _____

3. Which skills are sometimes hard for you to do?

   _____

   _____

4. Fill in the table below.

When you are doing math, does it help you to:	Yes	No
use manipulatives, like pattern blocks?		
work with a partner?		
work with a group?		
talk to your teacher?		
make a drawing of a problem?		
try a simpler problem?		
use a calculator?		
use a computer?		

Course 1

Beginning of Year Self-Assessment Survey (continued)

5. When you do work in math, do you like to work in a group, with a partner, or by yourself? Explain.

_____

_____

6. a. When you are working on a word problem, do you try using a problem solving strategy?

Yes _____   No _____

b. Check the strategies you know how to use.

_____ make a list   _____ solve a simpler problem

_____ draw a diagram   _____ simulate a problem

_____ guess and test   _____ solve by graphing

_____ look for a pattern   _____ work backward

_____ make a model   _____ write equations

c. Which strategies do you like the best?

_____

_____

d. Which strategies do you find most useful?

_____

_____

7. What do you do if you have trouble doing your math classwork?

_____

_____

8. What do you do if you have trouble doing your math homework?

_____

_____

9. a. What goal would you like to accomplish in math this year?

_____

_____

b. What might help you accomplish your goal?

_____

_____

◢ WHOLE NUMBERS: NUMERATION
Place Value

Read 86,200,721

Look at the digits in the place value chart below.

First, read each nonzero period of digits, starting on the left.
Then name the period.

BILLIONS			MILLIONS			THOUSANDS			ONES		
hundred billions	ten billions	billions	hundred millions	ten millions	millions	hundred thousands	ten thousands	thousands	hundreds	tens	ones
			8	6	2	0	0	7	2	1	

$\underline{86},$ $\underline{200},$ $\underline{721}$
↑   ↑   ↑

eighty-six million, two hundred thousand, seven hundred twenty-one
↑
Do not say *and.*

When a period contains only zeros, do not name it.

$\underline{5},$ 000, $\underline{203}$
↑   ↑

five million, two hundred three
↑
Do not say *thousand.*

Write each number in words.

1. 704 _____

2. 5,038 _____

3. 36,412 _____

4. 300,000 _____

5. 2,000,020 _____

6. 700,321,015 _____

_____

◼️◼️◼️WHOLE NUMBERS: NUMERATION
Periods in Place Value

In 1916, Jeannette Rankin of Missoula, Montana, achieved a notable first in American history. What was her achievement?

To solve:
1. Separate each numeral into proper periods by using commas.
2. Look at the number in the first period of each numeral. Find that number below and write the letter of the exercise above the number.

Example: E. 12057

Solution: 12,057   The first period is 12. Write *E* above 12.

Separate each numeral into proper periods by using commas.

S. 2368445	**A.** 59111743	**L.** 4785712
R. 882300121	**C.** 610555913	**S.** 93732744581
N. 7124500211713	**S.** 35400	**T.** 269777102
E. 23644810999152	**D.** 5912444	**T.** 478
G. 8826000914	**T.** 6101487312111	**I.** 9371145
O. 712481336	**O.** 3	**O.** 26911557382541
F. 236705554	**E.** 591112	**U.** 47857856855
S. 88200521	**R.** 61061061061	**C.** 937379
E. 71223891050	**M.** 354657687980	**N.** 1697005193618
	W. 40576811943641	

___ ___ ___ ___ ___   ___ ___ ___ ___ ___   ___ ___ ___ ___ ___ ___ _E_ ___
236 9   61 88 478   40 26 354 59   1   71   4 591 610 6   12   5

___ ___   ___ ___   ___ ___ ___ ___ ___ ___ ___ ___
269   3   47   35   937 712 7   8 882 23   2   93

◢WHOLE NUMBERS: NUMERATION
Writing Whole Numbers

Write in standard form: three million, one hundred two thousand.

The first period is millions.
Write 3 in the millions period.

___ ___ 3, ___ ___ ___, ___ ___ ___
millions   thousands   ones

The next period is thousands.
Write 102 in the thousands period.

___ ___ 3, 1 0 2, ___ ___ ___
millions   thousands   ones

Remember that each period, except for the leftmost period, must have three digits. Insert zeros for any missing digits. Since there are no digits for the ones period, write zeros to complete the number.

___ ___ 3, 1 0 2, 0 0 0
millions   thousands   ones

3 million 102 thousand
↓   ↓
___ ___ 3, 1 0 2, 0 0 0

For each word name, determine if the number is written correctly. If the number is correct, write *correct*. If it is not, write the correct number.

1. Two million, six hundred four thousand   2,604 _____

2. Three million, fifty-six thousand   3,056,000 _____

3. Eight hundred three million, thirty-seven   803,037 _____

4. Nine hundred fifteen billion   915,000,000 _____

Write each number in standard form.

5. Six thousand, thirty-two _____

6. Eight thousand, two _____

7. Seventy-three thousand _____

8. Fifty million, two hundred ninety-one _____

9. Eight million, twenty-five thousand _____

◤WHOLE NUMBERS: NUMERATION
Standard Form for Whole Numbers

Write each number in standard form, using commas.

1. eight thousand _____

2. six hundred eighty thousand, five hundred _____

3. one billion _____

4. nine hundred _____

5. two hundred eighty million, five hundred thousand _____

6. six hundred thousand, seven hundred _____

7. one thousand, two hundred _____

8. three thousand, three hundred _____

9. seven hundred four _____

10. fifty thousand _____

11. nine billion, five hundred thousand, seven hundred twenty-one _____

12. four hundred thousand, sixteen _____

13. twenty million, ninety thousand, six _____

14. three hundred million, nine hundred thousand _____

15. fifty thousand, forty-eight _____

16. eight hundred million, six thousand _____

17. seven trillion _____

18. five hundred three _____

19. four thousand eight _____

20. twenty-five thousand, twenty-three _____

WHOLE NUMBERS: NUMERATION
Comparing Whole Numbers

To compare two whole numbers, first count the number of digits. For example, a number with 4 digits is less than a number with 6 digits.

5,967 has 4 digits.
123,000 has 6 digits.
5,957 is less than 123,000.

38,940 has 5 digits.
406 has 3 digits.
38,940 is greater than 406.

$$5,957 < 123,000$$
↑
is less than

$$38,940 > 406$$
↑
is greater than

To compare two whole numbers with the same number of digits, compare the digits one at a time beginning at the left.

Example: Compare 2,482 and 2,495.

Solution: Compare each digit from left to right.   2,482
The thousands digits are equal.   2,495
The hundreds digits are equal.
The tens digits are *not* equal (8 < 9).
Therefore, 2,482 < 2,495.

Compare the two numbers. Write < or >.

1. 14,986 ____ 983

2. 34 ____ 492

3. 1,450 ____ 998

4. 137 ____ 132

5. 7,904 ____ 7,498

6. 38,011 ____ 3,999

7. 138,045 ____ 138,100

8. 6,847 ____ 6,874

9. 10,407 ____ 10,470

Write each set of numbers in order from least to greatest.

10. Bank check numbers: 205, 211, 199, 203, 197, 209, 207

_____

11. Invoice numbers: 3,892; 4,038; 4,003; 3,995; 4,007; 3,989

_____

12. Golf scores: 57, 98, 62, 94, 107, 78, 95, 86

_____

13. Attendance figures: 44,507; 28,491; 26,999; 46,995; 26,860; 65,892

_____

WHOLE NUMBERS: NUMERATION
Rounding Whole Numbers

Round 7,396 to the nearest ten.

Look at the number line at the right.
7,396 is closer to 7,400 than to 7,390.

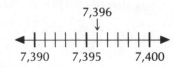

Round 89,882 to the nearest thousand.

89,882   Find the place to be rounded.
Look at the place to the right.
Since the digit is more than 5, round up.

Round up means round to the next higher digit.
There are 9 thousands, so the 9 becomes 10.
In this case, 89 becomes 90.

90,000   Write the rounded number under the original
number to be sure you have enough zeros.

Choose the correct answer.

1. Round 2,895 to the nearest ten.
   a. 2,800   **b.** 2,880   **c.** 2,900   **d.** 2,890   _____

2. Round 45,989 to the nearest thousand.
   a. 45,900   **b.** 46,000   **c.** 45,990   **d.** 45,000   _____

3. Round 3,896,716 to the nearest ten thousand.
   a. 3,900,000   **b.** 3,896,000   **c.** 3,890,000   **d.** 3,800,000   _____

4. Round 972,368 to the nearest hundred thousand.
   a. 900,000   **b.** 970,000   **c.** 1,000,000   **d.** 972,000   _____

Round each number to the nearest hundred thousand.

5. 5,821,634 _____   **6.** 9,987,431 _____

7. 48,399,260 _____   **8.** 964,308 _____

9. 3,937,792 _____   **10.** 968,048 _____

WHOLE NUMBERS: NUMERATION
Rounding Practice

One of the world's greatest adventure stories was first published in 1719 by the English writer Daniel Defoe. What was the book's title?

To solve:

1. Work each exercise.
2. Find the first digit of each rounded number to the left of the clue box. Find the second digit above the clue box. Find the letter at the intersection of the row and column.
3. Write that letter above the number of the exercise below.

	0	1	2	3	4
1	E	R	S	A	B
2	E	T	H	C	O
3	S	I	D	M	E
4	O	F	O	S	I
5	N	U	O	N	N
6	O	N	S	R	I
7	S	N	E	O	I
8	R	P	T	E	C

Example: 1. Round 53 to the nearest ten.

Solution: 50   The letter at the intersection of 5 and 0 is *N*. Write *N* above 1.

Round each of the following to the place indicated.

Ten:	2. 41 _____	3. 15 _____	4. 118 _____
Hundred:	5. 773 _____	6. 4,350 _____	7. 6,125 _____
Thousand:	8. 6,607 _____	9. 63,333 _____	10. 51,260 _____
Ten thousand:	11. 236,001 _____	12. 842,219 _____	
Hundred thousand:	13. 1,412,611 _____	14. 4,160,317 _____	

THE LIFE AND STRANGE SURPRISING ADVENTURES OF

__ __ __ __ __ __ __ N   __ __ __ __ __ __

9 2 13 6 7 4 11 1   12 5 10 8 14 3

▬▬WHOLE NUMBERS: NUMERATION
Interpreting Rounded Numbers

"About 4,500 people attended today's game."
"Over 4,500 people attended the game."
"Almost all of the 4,520 seats in the stadium were taken."

You often hear statements like these in news reports. What do
they mean? "About 4,500" usually means "closer to 4,500 than to
4,400 or 4,600." The expression *about 4,500* can be used to
describe any of the 100 whole numbers from 4,450 to 4,549.
When rounded to the nearest hundred, they all are "about 4,500."

4,450, 4,451, 4,452, . . . , 4,500, . . . , 4,547, 4,548, 4,549

| Least whole number that | Greatest whole number that |
| may be rounded to 4,500 | may be rounded to 4,500 |

The expression *over 4,500* can represent any number greater than
4,500. The least whole number "over 4,500" is 4,501.

4,501, 4,502, 4,503, . . .

The expression *almost 4,520* represents a number less than 4,520.
The greatest whole number that is "almost 4,520" is 4,519.

. . . , 4,517, 4,518, 4,519

Name the least whole number that each expression can represent.

1. About 300 _____   **2.** About 9,000 _____   **3.** Over 1,800 _____

2. About 960 _____   **5.** Over 1,250 _____   **6.** About 50 _____

**Name the greatest whole number that each expresison can
represent.**

7. About 400 _____   **8.** About 2,000 _____   **9.** Almost 100 _____

10. About 4,500 _____   **11.** Almost 8,000 _____   **12.** About 10,500 _____

**Name the greatest whole number that is being described. Name
the least whole number that is being described.**

*13. There are about 17,000 volumes in the city library. Over 17,200 books fill the shelves.
There are almost 17,500 books in the library.

greatest: _____   least: _____

WHOLE NUMBERS: OPERATIONS
Adding Whole Numbers

Add: 8,742 + 186 + 385

First, estimate the sum.

$$
\begin{array}{rcr}
8,742 & \rightarrow & 8,700 \\
186 & \rightarrow & 200 \\
+\quad 385 & \rightarrow & +\quad 400 \\
\hline
& & 9,300
\end{array}
$$

Round each addend to the greatest place of the smallest addend.
The smallest addend is 186.
The greatest place in 186 is hundreds.
Round all addends to the nearest hundred.
Add to estimate the sum.

Now add.

$$
\begin{array}{r}
8,742 \\
186 \\
+\quad 385 \\
\hline
9,313
\end{array}
$$

To check:

a. Compare the sum with the estimated sum. Is
9,313 close to 9,300? Yes.

b. Add up.
$$
\begin{array}{r}
8,742 \\
186 \\
+\quad 385 \\
\hline
9,313
\end{array}
$$

Write the estimated sum to the right of each problem. Then add and check.

1. $\begin{array}{r} 38 \\ +\ 27 \\ \hline \end{array}$ _____

2. $\begin{array}{r} 56 \\ +\ 21 \\ \hline \end{array}$ _____

3. $\begin{array}{r} 25 \\ 34 \\ +\ 87 \\ \hline \end{array}$ _____

4. $\begin{array}{r} 16 \\ 98 \\ +\ 44 \\ \hline \end{array}$ _____

5. $\begin{array}{r} 348 \\ +\ 267 \\ \hline \end{array}$ _____

6. $\begin{array}{r} 4,529 \\ +\ 3,874 \\ \hline \end{array}$ _____

7. $\begin{array}{r} 623 \\ 415 \\ +\ 381 \\ \hline \end{array}$ _____

8. $\begin{array}{r} 7,356 \\ 4,218 \\ +\ 5,033 \\ \hline \end{array}$ _____

9. $\begin{array}{r} 14,386 \\ +\ 27,121 \\ \hline \end{array}$ _____

WHOLE NUMBERS: OPERATIONS
Addition Practice

Bangui is the capital of an African country that gained its independence from France in 1960. Name the country.

To solve:
1. Work each exercise.
2. Find the first digit of each sum to the left of the answer box. Find the last digit above the answer box.
3. Write the letter of the exercise in the box at the intersection of the row and column.

Example: Add.   **A.** 92 + 44

Solution: 136   Write *A* in the box at the intersection of 1 and 6.

Add.

I. 21 + 13	**T.** 68 + 56	**A.** 174 + 182	**F.** 138 + 164	**E.** 91 + 91	**E.** 34 + 18

U. 366 + 198	**I.** 1,978 + 3,449	**L.** 2,888 + 2,408	**N.** 46,388 + 99,255	**L.** 2,539 + 7,648	**C.** 1,389 + 1,616

R. 5,723 7,669 + 4,953	**N.** 83,576 77,478 95,036 + 48,577	**A.** 568 953 729 + 1,131	**P.** 1,673 1,045 1,754 + 1,371	**C.** 8,045 23,641 17,873 + 7,699	**C.** 603,233 6,208,557 47,954 + 7,507,037

R. Add: 4,599 + 677 + 12,575 + 815 + 16,547 _____

R. Find the sum: 345; 2,579; 66; 721; 2,110 _____

	1	2	3	4	5	6	7	8
1						A		
3								
5				B				

WHOLE NUMBERS: OPERATIONS
Cross Number Puzzle

Complete each exercise. Then write the answers in the appropriate box in the cross number puzzle below.

Across	Down
2. 467 + 38 _____	**1.** 349 + 557 _____
4. 64,385 + 16,239 _____	**2.** 469,536 + 38,876 _____
6. 669 + 69 _____	**3.** 4,677 + 608 _____
7. 183 + 688 _____	**4.** 47,865 + 35,354 _____
9. 6,655 + 2,969 _____	**5.** 3,247 + 1,489 _____
10. 3,056 + 2,288 _____	**6.** 387 + 374 _____
11. 445 + 672 _____	**8.** 52 + 96 _____
13. 9 + 37 + 22 _____	**12.** 6,907 + 989 _____
14. 1,435 + 7,852 _____	**15.** 21 + 36 + 16 _____
16. 28 + 56 + 9 _____	

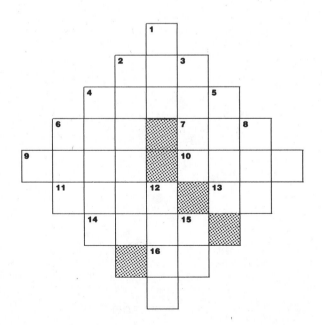

WHOLE NUMBERS: OPERATIONS
Subtracting Whole Numbers

Subtract: 308 − 57

First, estimate the difference.

Round each number to the greatest place of the smallest number.
The smallest number is 57.

$$308 \rightarrow \quad 310$$
$$-\ \ 57 \rightarrow -\ 60$$
$$\overline{\quad 250}$$

The greatest place in 57 is tens.
Round both numbers to the nearest ten.
Subtract to estimate the difference.

Now subtract.

$$\begin{array}{r} 308 \\ -\ 57 \\ \hline 1 \end{array}$$ 8 − 7 = 1

②⑩
$$\begin{array}{r} \cancel{3}\cancel{0}8 \\ -\ 57 \\ \hline 51 \end{array}$$ Regroup 3 hundreds as 2 hundreds 10 tens.
10 − 5 = 5

②⑩
$$\begin{array}{r} \cancel{3}\cancel{0}8 \\ -\ 57 \\ \hline 251 \end{array}$$ 2 − 0 = 2

To check:

a. Compare the difference with the estimated difference.
Is 251 close to 250? Yes.

b. Add the difference to the number subtracted.
The sum should be the number you subtracted from.

$$\begin{array}{r} 251 \\ +\ 57 \\ \hline 308 \end{array}$$

Write the estimated difference to the right of each problem. Then subtract and check.

1. 60 − 23	**2.** 72 − 28	**3.** 40 − 16	**4.** 360 − 72
5. 904 − 685	**6.** 700 − 519	**7.** 41,065 − 21,887	**8.** 50,381 − 19,872

WHOLE NUMBERS: OPERATIONS
Subtraction Practice

What is the popular name of Ludwig van Beethoven's Third Symphony?

To solve:

1. Work each exercise, transferring digits as indicated by arrows.
2. Match each number in the row of boxes below with a letter of the alphabet. Write the letter below the box.

Subtract.

1. 47
   − 5

2. 7□
   − 8

3. 8□
   − 32

4. 7□
   − 54

5. 87
   − 82

6. □0
   − 15

7. □7
   − 134

8. 7□4
   − 439

9. 768
   − 348

10. □00
   − 133

11. 6□8
   − 569

12. □44
   − 26

13. 8,119
   − 5,244

14. 9,46□
   − 5,838

15. □,□00
   − 1,525

16. 5,0□0
   − 2,861

17. 35,844
   − 12,513

18. 64,71□
   − 38,917

19. 77,00□
   − 38,855

20. 8□0,25□
   − 216,639

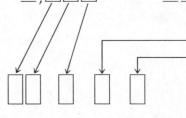

_____ _____ _____   _____ _____ _____   _____ _____ _____ _____

A	B	C	D	E	F	G	H	I	J	K	L	M	N	O	P	Q	R	S	T	U	V	W	X	Y	Z
1	2	3	4	5	6	7	8	9	10	11	12	13	14	15	15	17	18	19	20	21	22	23	24	25	26

17

◢▬WHOLE NUMBERS: OPERATIONS
Rules of Addition and Multiplication

1. The order in which you add or multiply doesn't matter.

$$2 + 3 = 3 + 2 \qquad 5 \times 9 = 9 \times 5$$

2. You can work with only two numbers at one time. If there are three or more numbers, you must pair them. Parentheses indicate how numbers are paired.

Think of $3 + 4 + 5$ as $(3 + 4) + 5$ or as $3 + (4 + 5)$.

Think of $6 \times 9 \times 3$ as $(6 \times 9) \times 3$ or as $6 \times (9 \times 3)$.

3. Adding two numbers and then multiplying their sum is the same as multiplying each addend and then adding the products.

$$2 \times (3 + 4) = (2 \times 3) + (2 \times 4)$$
$$2 \times 7 = 6 + 8$$
$$14 = 14$$

Complete the following.

1. $3 + 10 = 10 + \underline{\quad}$

2. $2 \times (3 \times 5) = (2 \times 3) \times \underline{\quad}$

3. $5 \times 21 = 21 \times \underline{\quad}$

4. $6 \times (3 + 9) = (\underline{\quad} \times 3) + (6 \times 9)$

5. $8 + (4 + 20) = (\underline{\quad} + 4) + 20$

6. $(9 \times 2) + (9 \times 8) = \underline{\quad} \times (2 + 8)$

7. $(7 \times 2) \times 5 = 7 \times (\underline{\quad} \times \underline{\quad})$

8. $(4 \times 3) + (4 \times 7) = \underline{\quad} \times (3 + \underline{\quad})$

Knowing these rules can help you calculate quickly in your head. For example, you can rearrange the numbers and work with convenient pairs.

Think of $2 + 11 + 8 + 9$ as $(2 + 8) + (11 + 9) = 10 + 20$, or 30.

Think of $8 \times 9 \times 5$ as $(8 \times 5) \times 9 = 40 \times 9$, or 360.

Think of 5×38 as $5 \times (30 + 8) = (5 \times 30) + (5 \times 8)$
$$= 150 + 40, \text{ or } 190.$$

Mentally rearrange the terms in the exercises below to simplify the arithmetic. Find the sum or product in your head. Write only the answer.

9. $13 + 9 + 7 + 1 = \underline{\qquad}$

10. $5 \times 47 = \underline{\qquad}$

11. $15 \times 7 \times 4 = \underline{\qquad}$

12. $4 \times 13 \times 25 \times 2 = \underline{\qquad}$

13. $(5 \times 68) + (5 \times 2) = \underline{\qquad}$

14. $7 \times (60 + 7) = \underline{\qquad}$

15. $9 \times 23 = \underline{\qquad}$

16. $9 \times (38 + 5) = \underline{\qquad}$

WHOLE NUMBERS: OPERATIONS
Multiplying With Zeros

Multiply: 280 × 9

First, estimate the product.

$$280 \rightarrow 300$$
$$\underline{\times9} \rightarrow \underline{\times9}$$
$$2{,}700$$

Round each factor to its greatest place.
Do not round one-digit factors.
Multiply to estimate the product.

Now multiply.

$$280$$
$$\underline{\times9}$$
$$2{,}520 \leftarrow 9 \times 0 = 0 \qquad \text{Don't forget to write 0 in the product.}$$

Check your answer.

$9 \times 0 = 0 \rightarrow$ product of the ones place
$9 \times 80 = 720 \rightarrow$ product of the tens place
$9 \times 200 = \underline{1{,}800} \rightarrow$ product of the hundreds place
$2{,}520$

Choose the correct product.

1. 700 × 3   **a.** 210   **b.** 2,100   **c.** 2,110   _____

2. 500 × 8   **a.** 4,000   **b.** 400   **c.** 40,000   _____

3. 2 × 600   **a.** 12,000   **b.** 120   **c.** 1,200   _____

4. 3,000 × 9   **a.** 30,000   **b.** 2,700   **c.** 27,000   _____

5. 4,200 × 5   **a.** 20,000   **b.** 21,000   **c.** 2,100   _____

Write the estimated product to the right of each problem. Then multiply and check.

6. $\quad$ 58
$\quad \underline{\times\ 4}$
$\quad$ _____

7. $\quad$ 79
$\quad \underline{\times\ 7}$
$\quad$ _____

8. $\quad$ 155
$\quad \underline{\times\ 2}$
$\quad$ _____

9. $\quad$ 702
$\quad \underline{\times\ 3}$
$\quad$ _____

10. $\quad$ 507
$\quad \underline{\times\ 3}$
$\quad$ _____

11. $\quad$ 620
$\quad \underline{\times\ 8}$
$\quad$ _____

WHOLE NUMBERS: OPERATIONS
Multiplying by One-Digit Numbers

The epic poem *The Aeneid* is about the wanderings of the Trojan hero Aeneas. Name the Roman poet who wrote it in the first century B.C.

To solve:

1. Work each exercise, transferring digits as indicated by arrows.
2. Match each number in the row of boxes below with a letter of the alphabet. Write the letter below the box.

Multiply.

1.
$$\begin{array}{r} 6 \\ \times\ 4 \\ \hline \end{array}$$
□ □
↓ ↓
□ □

2.

$$\times\ 3$$
□ □
↓ ↓
□ □

3.
□ □ 7
$$\times\qquad 9$$

□ , □
↓
□ 4

4.
$$\times\qquad 5$$
□ , □ □

5.
$$\begin{array}{r} 9 \\ \times\ 9 \\ \hline \end{array}$$
□
↓
□

6.
□ 9
$$\times\qquad 7$$
□ □
↓ ↓
□ □

7.
□ 2
$$\times\qquad 9$$
□ , □
↓
□ , 5 0 □

8.
$$\times\qquad 3$$
□ □
_ , □ □

9.
$$\begin{array}{r} 7 \\ \times\ 9 \\ \hline \end{array}$$
□

10.
□ 2
$$\times\qquad 8$$
□
↓
□

11.
7 1 □
$$\times\qquad 5$$
□ □
↓ ↓
□ , 6 2 □

12.
$$\times\qquad 2$$
□ , □

13.
$$\begin{array}{r} 8 \\ \times\ 6 \\ \hline \end{array}$$
□
↓
□

14.
□ 7
$$\times\qquad 4$$
□
↓
□

15.
2 , 6 □ 3
$$\times\qquad 5$$
□ □ □
↓ ↓
□ □
8 , □ □ 2

16.
$$\times\qquad 6$$
□ □
_ , □ □

□ □ □ □ □ □ □

___ ___ ___ ___ ___ ___ ___

A	B	C	D	I	F	G	H	I	J	K	L	M	N	O	P	Q	R	S	T	U	V	W	X	Y	Z
1	2	3	4	5	6	7	8	9	10	11	12	13	14	15	16	17	18	19	20	21	22	23	24	25	26

WHOLE NUMBERS: OPERATIONS
Partial Products

.Multiply: 328 × 54

```
  328     Multiply 328 by 4.
×  54     Write the partial product.
1 312     Write a zero directly under the ones place
    0     in the first partial product.
```

```
   328    Multiply 328 by 5.
×   54    Write that partial product to the
 1 312    left of the zero.
16 400    Add the two partial products.
17,712
```

Now check your answer by reversing the factors.

```
    54
× 328
   432
 1 080
16 200
17,712
```

Multiply. Then check your answer.

1. 71 × 16	**2.** 38 × 25	**3.** 49 × 73	**4.** 64 × 57
5. 216 × 84	**6.** 471 × 58	**7.** 376 × 97	**8.** 919 × 20
9. 4,285 × 61	**10.** 3,198 × 72	**11.** 8,836 × 125	**12.** 7,025 × 609
13. 4,008 × 309	**14.** 368 × 45,328	**15.** 49,218 × 607	**16.** 30,019 × 6,081

WHOLE NUMBERS: OPERATIONS
Multiplying by Numbers Greater Than 10

A Bavarian physicist discovered X-rays accidentally in 1895. Name the physicist.

To solve:
1. Work each exercise.
2. Look at the first two digits of each product. Find the same two digits below.
3. Write the letter of the exercise above the number each time it appears.

Example: Multiply.   E. 63×13

Solution: 819   Write *E* above 81.

Multiply.

A. 67
  × 15

E. 586
  × 22

N. 7,845
  × 35

L. 700
  × 41

D. 25
  × 34

L. 539
  × 63

E. 27,554
  × 57

G.   23
  × 8,477

O. 482
  × 241

H. 6,287
  × 853

R. 6,543
  × 1,278

N. 6,300
  × 92

I. 600
  × 900

N. 806
  × 255

M. 741
  × 605

C. 50,809
  × 508

T. 54×958 _____

O. Multiply 78 by 29. _____

W. 791×854 _____

R. Solve: $98 \times 48 = n$ _____

___ ___ ___ ___ E ___ ___   ___ ___ ___ ___ ___ ___
67 54 28 53 81 33 44   25 22 27 83 10 85

___ ___ ___ ___ ___ ___ ___ ___
47 11 12 20 51 19 15 57

Name_____ Class _____ Date _____

◢▀WHOLE NUMBERS: OPERATIONS
Zeros in the Quotient

Divide: 1,463 by 7

$$\begin{array}{r} 20 \\ 7\overline{)1,463} \\ 1\,4 \\ \hline 06 \end{array}$$

7 is greater than 1. Underline the 4 to help you remember where to put the first digit in the quotient.
$14 \div 7 = 2$. Write 2 over the underlined 4.
Multiply 7 by 2. Write 14 below 14 in the dividend. Then subtract.

Bring down the 6. 7 is greater than 6.
Write a zero above the 6.

$$\begin{array}{r} 209 \\ 7\overline{)1,463} \\ 1 \\ \hline 063 \\ 63 \\ \hline 0 \end{array}$$

Bring down the 3.
$63 \div 7 = 9$. Write 9 over the 3 in the dividend.
Multiply 7 by 9. Write 63 below 63 and subtract.
The remainder is zero.

Check your answer.

$$\begin{array}{r} 209 \\ \times \quad 7 \\ \hline 1,463 \end{array}$$

Choose the correct quotient.

1. $7\overline{)420}$ **a.** 6   **b.** 60   **c.** 16   _____

2. $2\overline{)1,012}$ **a.** 56   **b.** 156   **c.** 506   _____

3. $8\overline{)2,448}$ **a.** 136   **b.** 306   **c.** 36   _____

4. $3\overline{)3,240}$ **a.** 1,080   **b.** 18   **c.** 108   _____

Divide and check.

5. $6\overline{)408}$ **6.** $3\overline{)1,527}$ **7.** $4\overline{)828}$ **8.** $5\overline{)20,355}$

9. $7\overline{)39,221}$ **10.** $6\overline{)1,020}$ **11.** $9\overline{)7,434}$ **12.** $3\overline{)1,224}$

WHOLE NUMBERS: OPERATIONS
Dividing by One-Digit Divisors

**What American novelist wrote *The Deerslayer*
and *The Last of the Mohicans?***

To solve:

1. Work each exercise.
2. Look at the last two digits of each quotient. Find the same two digits below.
3. Write the letter of the exercise above the number each time it appears.

Example: Divide.   **J.** 6)$\overline{426}$

Solution: 71   Write *J* above 71.

Divide.

S. 4)$\overline{48}$ **I.** 3)$\overline{234}$ **R.** 8)$\overline{512}$

N. 7)$\overline{854}$ **E.** 2)$\overline{1,390}$ **P.** 5)$\overline{4,165}$

M. 9)$\overline{19,305}$ **O.** 6)$\overline{35,418}$ **C.** 7)$\overline{49,203}$

A. 3)$\overline{18,078}$ **F.** 6)$\overline{49,512}$ **O.** 4)$\overline{10,024}$

E. 9)$\overline{32,175}$ **M.** 7)$\overline{56,861}$ **R.** 8)$\overline{33,504}$

$\underset{71}{\text{J}}$ ___ ___ ___ ___   ___ ___ ___ ___ ___ ___ ___ ___
71 26 23 75 12   52 95 22 78 45 03 64 75

___ ___ ___ ___ ___ ___
29 03 06 33 95 88

WHOLE NUMBERS: OPERATIONS
Positioning the Quotient, Two-Digit Divisors

Divide: 23,568 by 58

```
      40
58)23,568
   23 2
      36
```

58 is greater than 2 or 23, so divide 58 into 235. Underline the 5 to help you remember where to put the first digit in the quotient.

Think: 58 rounds to 60, and 235 rounds to 240. Try 4. Write 4 above the underlined 5.

Multiply: 4 × 58 = 232. Subtract.
58 is greater than 3. Bring down the 6.
58 is greater than 36. Write a zero above the 6.

```
      406 R20
58)23,568
   23 2
      368
      348
       20
```

Bring down the 8.
Think: 58 rounds to 60, and 368 rounds to 370.
Write 6 above the 8.
Multiply: 6 × 58 = 348. Subtract.
The remainder is 20.

Check your answer.

```
     406
   ×  58
   3 248
  20 30
  23 548
+     20 ←Remember to add the remainder.
  23,568
```

In each dividend, the underlined digit is the one over which you should write the first digit of the quotient. Write *true* or *false*.

1. 37)4,9$\underline{3}$8 _____

2. 97)$\underline{8}$6,521 _____

3. 105)368,1$\underline{0}$0 _____

4. 329)31,4$\underline{6}$5 _____

Divide and check.

5. 32)864

6. 95)6,941

7. 67)20,721

8. 58)406,290

9. 38)21,715

10. 81)49,400

WHOLE NUMBERS: OPERATIONS
Dividing by Numbers Greater Than 10

What was the famous tribute to George Washington uttered by General "Light Horse Harry" Lee at Washington's funeral in 1799?

To solve:

1. Work each exercise.
2. In the clue box find the word that matches each quotient.
3. Write the word above the number of the exercise each time it appears below.

Example: Divide.   **1.** $13\overline{)416}$

Solution: 32   The word *of* matches 32. Write *of* above 1.

Divide.

3—first
6—woman
8—family
13—child
18—peace
19—in
32—of
83—and
85—now
87—an
128—the
214—his
230—never
232—victory
234—defeat
251—patriots
287—soldiers
462—minds
465—hearts
801—citizens
806—countrymen
808—elephants
1,321—first
2,416—war
2,511—death
2,614—life

2. $21\overline{)1,743}$ **3.** $83\overline{)1,577}$

4. $67\overline{)8,576}$ **5.** $75\overline{)16,050}$

6. $57\overline{)75,297}$ **7.** $88\overline{)212,608}$

8. $317\overline{)951}$ **9.** $476\overline{)8,568}$

10. $233\overline{)108,345}$ **11.** $304\overline{)245,024}$

"_____ _____ _____ , _____ _____
   6   3   7   8   3

_____ , _____ _____ _____ _____
   9   2   6   3   4

_____   OF   _____ _____ ."
  10   5   11

WHOLE NUMBERS
Mixed Review, Form A

Write in words.

1. 20,497 _____

2. 687,502,000 _____

   _____

3. 3,460,005 _____

Write the standard form using commas.

4. Thirty-two billion, six hundred eighteen million, nine thousand, twelve _____

5. Four hundred forty-three million, seventy-five thousand _____

Round to the place indicated.

6. 742 to the nearest ten _____

7. 586,598 to the nearest thousand _____

8. 8,397,641 to the nearest ten thousand _____

Add.

9.   26,591
       32,788
      + 10,456

10. 348 + 670 + 496 + 285 _____

11. 5,674 + 62 + 817 + 39 _____

Subtract.

12.   71,632
      − 48,755

13. 300,000 − 176,278 _____

14. Take 26,593 from 50,218. _____

Multiply.

15. 285 × 697 _____

16.   3,657
      ×   4

17.   893
      × 56

Divide.

18. $8\overline{)3,672}$

19. $28\overline{)10,192}$

WHOLE NUMBERS
Mixed Review, Form B

Use the following problem to answer exercises 1, 2, and 3.

Mr. Roberts traveled 4 days, averaging 395 kilometers per day. He drove for 7 hours each day. How many kilometers did he travel in the 4 days?

1. What facts are not needed to solve the problem? _____

2. What operation is needed to solve the problem? _____

3. What is the answer? _____

4. Is 1,265 a reasonable answer if the estimate is 1,000? _____

5. Write 37,485,000 in words. _____

_____

6. Write nine hundred thirty-four million, sixty-two thousand, five hundred in

   standard form. _____

7. Round 476,029 to the nearest ten thousand. _____

8.
```
   29,356
   48,291
 + 65,038
```

9. $639 + 741 + 390 + 506$ _____

10. $2,349 + 685 + 19 + 5,078 + 364$ _____

11.
```
   63,405
 − 26,788
```

12. $80,000 − 42,376$ _____

13. Take 2,984 from 5,614. _____

14.
```
   2,769
 ×     8
```

15. $5,068 × 9$ _____

16.
```
    637
 ×   18
```

17. $436 × 279$ _____

18. $6\overline{)3,042}$

19. $32\overline{)7,936}$

20. $316\overline{)40,448}$

■▬MEASUREMENT
Metric Units Of Length

The basic metric unit of length is the **meter (m)**.

 1,000 meters (m) = 1 kilometer (km)
 100 centimeters (cm) = 1 meter (m)
 10 millimeters (mm) = 1 centimeter (cm)
 1,000 millimeters (mm) = 1 meter (m)

A meter is about the length of one giant step.
A centimeter is about the width of a jumbo paper clip.
A millimeter is about the thickness of 3 index cards.
A kilometer is used to measure distances, such as the distance between two cities.

Use a centimeter ruler. Measure each line segment in centimeters.
Example: 3 cm and 5 mm = 3.5 cm

1. _____

2. _____

3. _____

4. _____

5. _____

Use a centimeter ruler. Draw each line segment.

6. 7 cm

7. 25 mm

8. 6.4 cm

9. 8.2 cm

10. 1 cm

© Prentice-Hall, Inc.

■MEASUREMENT
Metric Units Of Mass

The basic metric unit of mass is the **gram (g).**
On Earth, mass is usually the same as weight.

1,000 milligrams (mg) = 1 gram (g)
    1,000 grams (g) = 1 kilogram (kg)
  1,000 kilograms (kg) = 1 metric ton (t)

A dollar bill has a mass of about 1 g.
A grain of salt has a mass of about 1 mg.
A duckling has a mass of about 1 kg.
A sports car has a mass of about 1 t.

To change to a smaller unit, multiply.
    7.5 kg = ___ g
    7.5 x 1,000 = 7,500
    7.5 kg = 7,500 g

To change to a larger unit, divide.
    850 mg = ___ g
    850 ÷ 1,000 = 0.850, or 0.85
    850 mg = 0.85 g

Complete each sentence. Tell whether you would multiply or divide.

1. To change grams to milligrams, you would _____ by _____.

2. To change grams to kilograms, you would _____ by _____.

**Would you use milligrams, grams, or kilograms to measure each of
the following?**

3. a crayon _____   4. a duck's feather _____

5. 6 large apples _____   6. a baseball player _____

Complete.

7. 84 g = ___ mg   8. 3.4 kg = ___ g   9. 654 g = ___ kg

10. 802 g = ___ kg   11. 4.7 t = ___ kg   12. 750 mg = ___ g

▬MEASUREMENT
Metric Units Of Capacity

The basic metric unit of capacity is the **liter (L).**

1,000 milliliters (mL) = 1 liter (L)
    1,000 liters (L) = 1 kiloliter (kL)

A few drops of food coloring are about 1 mL.
Large bottles of soda pop come in containers of 2 L.
Water in a swimming pool could be measured in kiloliters.

To change to a smaller unit, multiply.

3.5 kL = ___ L
3.5 x 1,000 = 3,500
3.5 kL = 3,500 L

To change to a larger unit, divide.

1,750 mL = ___ L
1,750 ÷ 1,000 = 1.75
1,750 mL = 1.75L

Complete each sentence. Tell whether you would multiply or divide.

1. To change liters to milliliters, you would _____ by _____.

2. To change milliliters to liters, you would _____ by _____.

Would you use milliliter, liter, or kiloliter to measure the contents of each of the following?

3. a bottle of perfume _____

4. gasoline in a car's tank _____

5. water stored in a water tank _____

6. a travel-size bottle of shampoo _____

Complete.

7. 8,400mL = ___ L   **8.** 35,400 L = ___ kL   **9.** 6.54 kL = ___ L

10. 802 L = ___ mL   **11.** 7.5 kL = ___ L   **12.** 2,750 mL = ___ L

MEASUREMENT
Relating Metric Units

Tell which metric unit you could reasonably use to measure each item.

1. the distance between two cities _____ kilometer _____

2. the length of a ladybug _____

3. 6 drops of cough medicine _____

4. a load of bricks for a patio _____

5. the water in an Olympic-sized swimming pool _____

6. the distance around a running track _____

7. a raindrop _____

8. water in a full bathtub _____

9. the weight of a basketball player _____

10. the flying altitude of a jumbo jet _____

11. the mass of a bus _____

12. the distance from Canada to Mexico _____

13. the mass of a ballpoint pen _____

14. a large melon _____

15. length of a skateboard _____

16. the mass of a dollar bill _____

17. the width of a dollar bill _____

18. the thickness of a dollar bill _____

19. the diameter of a half dollar _____

20. the mass of a strand of hair _____

MEASUREMENT
Converting Measures of Time

Change 10 years to days.

First, determine the number of leap years in 10 years. Divide 10 by 4, since every fourth year is a leap year. Disregard the fractional part of your answer.

$$10 \div 4 = 2\frac{1}{2} \rightarrow 2$$

There are 2 leap years in a period of 10 years.

1 year = 365 days
1 leap year = 366 days

$(2 \times 366) + (8 \times 365)$ Multiply 366 by 2.
     732 + 2,920   Multiply 365 by the remaining 8 years.
       3,652 days   Add the products.

There are 3,652 days in 10 years.

Complete each sentence.

1. When changing several years to days, use _____ days for every fourth year to account for leap year.

2. There are _____ days in 5 years.

3. There are 2,556 days in _____ years.

Complete.

4. $3\frac{1}{2}$ h = _____ min

5. 360 h = _____ da

6. 9 yr = _____ da

7. 2 da 8 h = _____ h

8. 180 mo = _____ yr

9. $1\frac{1}{2}$ yr = _____ mo

Solve.

10.   12 h 37 min
     + 8 h 25 min

11.   3 min 7 s
     − 2 min 28 s

12.   8 yr 3 mo
         × 9

13. $4\overline{)5\text{ wk 5 da}}$

▰▰MEASUREMENT
Reading a Timetable

Leave	Arrive	Flight	Stops	Meals	Leave	Arrive	Flight	Stops	Meals
From: DALLAS-FORT WORTH (CST)					From: DALLAS-FORT WORTH (CST)				
TO: CHICAGO (CST)					TO: MIAMI (EST)				
6 30a	9 15a	242	One-Stop	M	8 35a	12 00n	79	Non-Stop	M
8 20a	10 15a	54	Non-Stop	M	12 05p	3 25p	63	Non-Stop	M
10 20a	2 10p	248	Two-Stops	S	5 00p	9 10p	169	One-Stop	M
2 40p	5 30p	140	One-Stop	S	8 10p	12 15a	405	One-Stop	S
3 20p	5 20p	44	Non-Stop	S	TO: NEW ORLEANS (CST)				
5 20p	7 20p	36	Non-Stop	M	8 35a	9 45a	157	Non-Stop	M
7 15p	10 45p	120/156	Kansas City	M	11 30a	12 40p	235	Non-Stop	M
TO: DENVER (MST)					4 40p	5 50p	133	Non-Stop	S
9 25a	10 05a	62	Non-Stop	M	TO: SEATTLE-TACOMA (PST)				
11 25a	12 05p	68	Non-Stop	M	11 30a	1 10p	95	Non-Stop	M
4 25p	5 30p	66	One-Stop	S	6 40p	8 20p	182	Non-Stop	M
6 25p	7 05p	78	Non-Stop	M	7 45p	10 20p	184	One-Stop	M

How long does it take Flight 184 to go from Dallas-Fort Worth to Seattle-Tacoma?
The flight leaves Dallas-Fort Worth at 7:45 P.M. CST and arrives in Seattle-Tacoma at 10:20 P.M. PST.

First, find the arrival time in CST.
Remember: CST is 2 hours later than PST.

10:20 P.M. PST is equivalent to 12:20 A.M. CST.

7:45 P.M. to midnight→ 4 h 15 min	elapsed time from 7:45 P.M. to midnight
midnight to 12:20 A.M.→ + 20 min	elapsed time from midnight to 12:20 A.M
4 h 35 min	Add to find total elapsed time.

Choose the correct answer.

1. How long does it take Flight 169 to fly from Dallas-Fort Worth to Miami?

a. 5 h 10 min   **b.** 3 h 10 min   **c.** 4 h 10 min   _____

Solve.

2. What time does Flight 79 leave Dallas-Fort Worth for Miami? _____

3. What time does it arrive in Miami? _____

4. How long does the trip take? _____

◣MEASUREMENT
Reading Thermometer Scales

Many instruments, such as thermometers and scales, have measurement scales that are marked in tenths or hundredths. The little marks on a measurement scale are called *graduations*; the numbers are called *calibrations*. A scale that is calibrated in tenths or hundredths is called a *decimal scale*.

The first thermometer shown below gives a temperature in degrees Celsius. Each 1° interval is divided into 10 smaller intervals of 0.1° each. The reading at point *A* is 37.5°C.

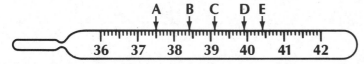

The second thermometer below gives a temperature in degrees Fahrenheit. To read a temperature on this scale, you must first determine what each graduation represents.

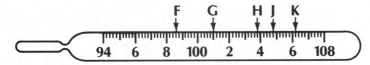

Example: On the second thermometer, what is the reading at point *F*?

Solution: Each 1° interval is divided into 5 smaller intervals. Since 10 ÷ 5 = 2, each smaller interval represents 0.2°. Count by 0.2 beginning with 98.0. The reading at *F* is 98.6°F.

Use the thermometers above to find the reading indicated by each letter.

1. *B* _____   **2.** *C* _____   **3.** *D* _____   **4.** *E* _____

5. *G* _____   **6.** *H* _____   **7.** *J* _____   **8.** *K* _____

Use the scales at the right to find the letter that corresponds to each reading.

9. 0.9 _____   **10.** 0.3 _____

11. 0.6 _____   **12.** 0.2 _____

13. 0.25 _____   **14.** 0.10 _____

15. 0.85 _____   **16.** 0.45 _____

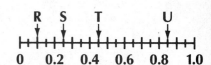

PROBLEM SOLVING
Reading to Understand a Problem

1. Rewrite the following problem in your own words.
   The largest gold nugget ever found weighed $472\frac{1}{2}$ pounds. The largest known topaz weighs 596 pounds. What is the difference in weight between the two?

   _____

2. Find the given facts in the following problem.
   It cost Guillermo Diaz $4.33 to mail a box of books. The mailing rate was 42¢ for the first pound and 17¢ for each additional pound. How heavy was the box?

   _____

3. What is the question in the following problem?
   How much did Susan save by buying a $43 sweater on sale for $26?

   _____

4. Which fact is not needed to solve each problem?
   a. Luke Stevens's living room measures 4 yards by 6 yards. Carpet costs $9 per square yard. Luke spent $288 on carpet. How many square yards of carpet did he buy?

   _____

   b. Each of the 36 chimpanzees in the zoo eats 8 bananas per day. If a banana weighs 9 ounces, how many bananas are eaten each day?

   _____

5. Are enough facts given to solve each problem? If not, which fact is missing?
   a. Andy Duncan types at the rate of 62 words per minute. How long will it take him to type his history term paper?

   _____

   b. Mrs. Tanaka planted 20 acres of wheat. Each acre yielded 62 bushels. If she sold all of the wheat, how much money did she earn?

   _____

6. According to its title, what does the table show?

   _____

FUEL CONSUMPTION (MI/GAL)

Model	Rate of speed (mi/h)			
	35	45	55	65
Compact	39	38	35	30
Mid-size	31	30	28	25
Luxury	26	24	21	17

7. What specific information is presented in the table?

   _____

▬◢PROBLEM SOLVING
Missing Information

Good problem solvers understand the value of sorting important facts from those that are unimportant. They can also identify what information is missing.

   Use the following procedure to help identify which facts are useful and which are missing.

1. Read the problem at least once to identify the question.
2. Read the problem again to sort the given facts into two categories: important and not important.
3. Ask the question, "Do I have all the information I need to solve the problem?"
   • If the answer is yes, make a plan, solve, and check.
   • If the answer is no, determine what information is missing.

Read each problem, then list all the important facts and identify the missing information.

1. Abraham Lincoln was assassinated on April 15, 1865. How old would he have been on April 15, 1900, if he had still been alive?

   Important facts: _____

   Missing information: _____

2. Carol Wright has a set of eight 12-ounce glasses. How many glasses can she fill with 1 container of milk?

   Important facts: _____

   Missing information: _____

3. Frank Jackson is 5 feet 7 inches tall. How much shorter is he than the tallest recorded human being?

   Important facts: _____

   Missing information: _____

4. A can of paint covers an area of 900 square feet. How many cans will you need to put two coats of paint on your bedroom walls?

   Important facts: _____

   Missing information: _____

◤ PROBLEM SOLVING
Hidden Questions

For each problem, write the question that, when answered, will provide the information needed to solve the problem.

1. There are 88 keys on a piano, including 52 white keys. How many more white keys than black keys are there? _____

2. Pierre Roberts is painting a 50-yard-long fence that has 6 posts per yard. He can paint 10 posts with a quart of paint. How much paint does he need to paint the fence?

_____

3. Elaine Moore drove 385 miles at 55 miles per hour. If she played the radio for 20 minutes each hour, how long was the radio on during her trip?

_____

For each problem, use the given facts to find the information needed to solve the problem.

4. Derek Lewis is 17, which is 29 years younger than his father. His father is twice as old as Derek's brother Patrick. How old is Patrick? _____

5. Fritz Barnes sells eggs for $.81 a dozen. One morning, he sold 1,020 eggs. How much money did he make? _____

6. Kevin Atkins wants to work two days and earn $100. The first day, he works 8 hours at $6.50 per hour. How much money must he make the second day in order to reach his goal? _____

Solve.

7. Lupe Moreno has been running for $1\frac{3}{4}$ hours at 8 miles per hour. If she plans to run 20 miles, how much further does she have to run? _____

8. Marcy Skillman loaded boxes into her truck, each box containing six 15-pound turkeys. Her truck can safely transport 1,350 pounds of cargo. What is the maximum number of boxes she can carry? _____

9. A movie theater has 42 rows of seats with 24 seats in each row. At one performance, all but 20 tickets were sold. Find the amount brought in on ticket sales if the price of a ticket was $4. _____

PROBLEM SOLVING
Making a Plan

The answer to a word problem may not be obvious, but the *kind* of answer expected usually is obvious. If the question is "What time is it?" then the answer should be a time of day.

   When you read a problem, ask yourself: "What is the question? What kind of answer is expected?" For example, if the expected answer is a measurement, ask: "What kind of measurement is expected? What unit of measurement is expected?" If the expected answer is a number, ask: "What is being counted?"

For each question, think about what kind of answer is expected. Then choose the best kind of answer from the box below.

1. How many people attended the game? _____

2. How much higher is Mt. Everest than Mt. Fuji? _____

3. Who finished first in the roller derby? _____

4. How long has this magazine been published? _____

5. Is Austin, Texas, more populated than New York City? _____

an ordinal number	a length of time
a measure of height	the name of a location
a time of day	a whole number
the name of a person	yes or no

For each question, think about what kind of answer is expected. Then choose the best answer from the box at the right.

6. What is the price of admission? _____

7. How long is this pencil? _____

8. How many passengers are in the car? _____

9. What time does the game start? _____

10. How often will I be paid? _____

11. In what place did a runner finish? _____

2:00 P.M.
2 people
2 cm
2 cars
2 times per month
2 tickets
second
$2.00

◼️▬ PROBLEM SOLVING
Solve a Simpler Problem

Solve each problem by first solving a simpler problem.

1. Baker Bill slices a flat sheet of dough into narrow strips to make strudel. If Bill makes 73 cuts in the dough, how many strips will he obtain? _____

2. The Duke of Albuquerque is honored with a 21-gun salute. If 5 seconds elapse between gunshots, how long will it take to honor the duke? _____

3. Han-Chow Ding arrived at Cozy Lake on the 9th day of his summer vacation and departed on the 74th day. How many days was Han-Chow at the lake? _____

4. If 1 followed by 5 zeros (100,000) is multiplied by 1 followed by 7 zeros, and the result is multiplied by 1 followed by 16 zeros, how many zeros will there be in the product? _____

5. A scallop shell has small curved arcs at its end, separated by straight ribs. If a scallop shell has 66 ribs, how many arcs does it have? _____

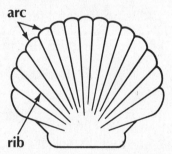

6. To the right is a 5-sided prism with a diagonal drawn from one vertex. How many diagonals could you draw from a vertex of a 35-sided prism?

_____

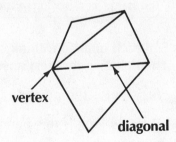

7. Yolanda Mosso is attempting to swim across Enchantment Bay. Each minute she swims forward 112, feet but the tide pushes her back 23 feet. If the bay is 2,047 feet wide, how long will it take Yolanda to complete her swim? _____

8. In the nation of Inflation, the first pickle you buy costs 1¢, the second 2¢, the third 4¢, the fourth 8¢, and so on, with the price doubling for each additional pickle. How much will 12 pickles cost? (Hint: Calculate the cost of 3 pickles, 4 pickles, and 5 pickles. Can you find a shortcut for figuring these costs?) _____

Name_____ Class _____ Date _____

PROBLEM SOLVING
Checking the Answer

To check your solution to a problem, reread the problem and look
at your answer. Ask yourself: "Has the question been answered? Is
the answer suitable?"

Example: Read the problem but do not solve it. Look at the possible
answers and choose the one that is suitable.

At 9:00 A.M. the temperature outside was 32°F.
By 1:00 P.M. the temperature had increased 8°.
What was the temperature at 1:00 P.M.?
a. 24°F   **b.** 4 h   **c.** 40°F

Solution: **a.** Because the temperature increased, the answer must be
higher than 32°F, so **a** is not suitable.
b. Because temperature is not measured in hours, **b** is not
suitable.
c. 40 is greater than 32, and the unit of measure is correct,
so **c** is a suitable answer.

**Read each problem but do not solve it. Tell whether each answer
is suitable. If an answer is not suitable, explain why.**

1. On August 28, 1981, Sebastian Coe ran the fastest outdoor mile with a time of 3 minutes
47.33 seconds. On July 27, 1985, Steve Cram broke Coe's record with a time of 3 minutes
46.31 seconds. For how many days did Sebastian Coe hold the world record?

   a. 0.02 second _____

   b. 5 years _____

   c. 1,794 days _____

   d. 3 years 10 months 30 days _____

   _____

2. An official baseball must weigh no less than 5 ounces; its circumference must be no less
than 9 inches. An official basketball must weigh no more than 22 ounces; its circumference
must be no greater than 30 inches. What are the greatest possible differences in the weights
and circumferences of an official baseball and an official basketball?

   a. 7 ounces _____

   b. 17 ounces; 21 inches _____

   c. 21 inches _____

   d. 5 pounds _____

© Prentice-Hall, Inc.

41

PROBLEM SOLVING
A Method of Estimation

Different situations require different ways of estimating. When you want to estimate the amount of money that you need for a project, you should overestimate. When you want to estimate the amount of money you *have* for a project, you should underestimate.

Suppose you are buying a number of items in a store. You can estimate the total cost by finding a range of numbers that will include it. First, overestimate the total cost, then underestimate it. The actual total cost will be between these two extremes.

Example: The following numbers represent the costs of an art project: $128.92, $14.31, $9.19, $26.25.
  a. Use multiples of $10 to overestimate the total.
  b. Use multiples of $10 to underestimate the total.
  c. State a range within which the actual total must fall.

Solution: **a.** Round all numbers up to the next greater $10.

$130 + $20 + $10 + $30 = $190

$190 is the maximum total of the project.

b. Round all numbers down to the next lower $10.

$120 + $10 + $0 + $20 = $150

$150 is the minimum total of the project.

c. The actual total must be between $150 and $190.

Follow the directions below for exercises 1–4.
a. Use multiples of $10 to overestimate the total.
b. Use multiples of $10 to underestimate the total.
c. State a range within which the actual total must fall.

1. $98.57, $13.40, $54.38

a. _____

b. _____

c. _____

2. $14.12, $134.98, $15.19, $74.49

a. _____

b. _____

c. _____

3. $25.34, $47.24, $13.96, $253.28

a. _____

b. _____

c. _____

4. $47.24, $308.19, $45.16, $247.99

a. _____

b. _____

c. _____

◢PROBLEM SOLVING
Estimating the Answer

In each of the following, choose a method of computation and estimate the answer.

1. 23 + 27   **2.** 68 − 45   **3.** 49 + 31   **4.** 139 − 62

_____   _____   _____   _____

5. 8 × 7 _____   **6.** 63 ÷ 9 _____   **7.** 16 × 10 _____   **8.** 88 ÷ 22 _____

9. Which is greater, 58 + 79 or 131? _____ **10.** Which is less, 47 or 83 − 44? _____

11. Which is less, 162 − 83 or 75? _____ **12.** Which is greater, 19 × 9 or 200? _____

13. 421 + 532   **14.** 879 + 613

_____   _____

15. 514 + 220 + 613   **16.** 898 + 467 + 910

_____   _____

17. 545 − 213   **18.** 781 − 596

_____   _____

19. 462 − 359   **20.** 6,548 − 1,387

_____   _____

21. 12 × 9   **22.** 48 × 71

_____   _____

23. 712 × 87   **24.** 478 × 116

_____   _____

25. 826 × 387   **26.** 146 ÷ 5

_____   _____

27. 912 ÷ 29   **28.** 591 ÷ 21

_____   _____

29. 3,177 ÷ 193   **30.** 4,821 ÷ 248

_____   _____

31. 43 + 161 + 79 + 214 + 98 _____

32. 9 × 21 × 12 × 48 _____

◢ PROBLEM SOLVING
Reasonable Answers

Circle the estimate that makes the answer reasonable.

1. The answer 33 is reasonable if the estimate is: 40   4   400

2. The answer 6 is reasonable if the estimate is: 10   50   500

3. The answer 19 is reasonable if the estimate is: 10   100   1,000

4. The answer 844 is reasonable if the estimate is: 500   84   8,400

5. The answer 150 is reasonable if the estimate is: 15   200   500

6. The answer 600 is reasonable if the estimate is: 6   100   750

7. The answer 990 is reasonable if the estimate is: 99   1,000   9,000

8. The answer 41 is reasonable if the estimate is: 8   50   100

9. The answer 2,100 is reasonable if the estimate is: 200   21   3,000

10. The answer 82 is reasonable if the estimate is: 8,000   75   200

11. The answer 5,722 is reasonable if the estimate is: 4,500   14,000   57

12. The answer 9,000 is reasonable if the estimate is: 8,000   19,000   900

13. The answer 469 is reasonable if the estimate is: 100   50   600

14. The answer 17,965 is reasonable if the estimate is: 20,000   50,000   1,700

15. The answer 3,611 is reasonable if the estimate is: 360   36   4,500

16. The answer 24,777 is reasonable if the estimate is: 60,000   40,000   20,000

17. The answer 8,900 is reasonable if the estimate is: 700   7,000   70,000

18. The answer 249,555 is reasonable if the estimate is: 98,000   39,000   300,000

19. The answer 11,111 is reasonable if the estimate is: 6,000   14,000   40,000

20. The answer 27,956 is reasonable if the estimate is: 21   21,000   50,000

21. The answer 3,333 is reasonable if the estimate is: 300   3,000   30,000

22. The answer 145 is reasonable if the estimate is: 100   50   500

Practice

1. Choose a page from a book you are reading. Choose 50 words on that page. Using these 50 words, complete the frequency table.

Letter	Tally	Frequency
t		
s		
r		
n		
d		

2. Make a line plot for your frequency table.

3. Which letter occurred most frequently in your sample? Least frequently? _____

Use the line plot at the right to answer each question.

4. What information is displayed in the line plot?

_____

5. How many students spent time doing homework last night?

_____

6. How many students spent at least a half hour on homework?

_____

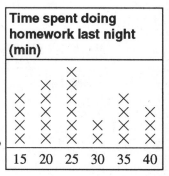

Time spent doing homework last night (min)

15 20 25 30 35 40

7. What is the range of time spent on homework last night?

_____

8. A kennel is boarding dogs that weigh the following amounts (in pounds).
What is the range of the dogs' weights? _____

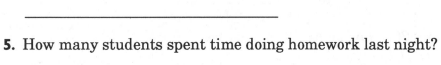

| 5 | 62 | 43 | 48 | 12 | 17 | 29 | 74 |
| 8 | 15 | 4 | 11 | 15 | 26 | 63 | |

9. How many of the dogs weigh under 50 lb? _____

■■■■**Practice**

Make a table to solve each problem.

1. How many ways are possible to make change for 36¢?

   _____

2. Tom has a $20 bill, a $10 bill, a $5 bill, and a $1 bill. List all the prices of items he could buy if he receives no change.

   _____

3. A club began with 4 members. At each meeting every member must bring 2 other new people. These new people become members. How many members will there be after 3 meetings?

   _____

4. Colleen is making raffle tickets for the school's give-away drawing. She wants to use the digits 2, 5, 7, and 8 to make three-digit numbers. How many different three-digit numbers can she make if she can use each digit any number of times?

   _____

Use any strategy to solve each problem. Show all your work.

5. Gavin sells popcorn at basketball games. A large box costs $.75, and a small box costs $.40. One night he sold 45 boxes and collected a total of $25. How many large and how many small boxes of popcorn did Gavin sell?

   _____

6. Find the total number of triangles in the figure. _____

7. How many squares are contained in the floor tile below? _____

8. Find the smallest number that meets all of the following criteria. _____

   • when you divide the number by 5 there is 3 left over

   • when you divide the number by 8 there is 2 left over

   • when you divide the number by 9 there is 4 left over

▬▬▬▬Practice

Find the mean, median, and mode for each set of data.

Data

1. 85, 91, 76, 85, 93

2. 72, 76, 73, 74, 75

3. 5, 7, 9, 10, 9, 9, 10, 5

4. 129, 156, 118, 147, 131, 129

5. 86, 87, 95, 96, 88, 94, 98

Mean	Median	Mode
____	____	____
____	____	____
____	____	____
____	____	____
____	____	____

6. What is the mean height of the active volcanoes listed? (Find the mean to the nearest foot.)

_____

7. What is the median height of the active volcanoes listed?

_____

8. What is the mode of the heights of the active volcanoes listed?

_____

Active Volcanoes

Name	Height above Sea Level (ft)
Camaroon Mt.	13,354
Mount Erebus	12,450
Asama	8,300
Gerde	9,705
Sarychev	5,115
Ometepe	5,106
Fogo	9,300
Mt. Hood	11,245
Lascar	19,652

Source: The Universal Almanac

9. What is the mean of the wages listed?

_____

10. What is the median of the wages listed?

_____

11. What is the mode of the wages listed?

_____

Hourly Wages of Production Workers (includes benefits) 1991

Country	Wage
Austria	$17.47
Brazil	$2.55
Finland	$20.57
France	$15.26
Hong Kong	$3.58
Japan	$14.41
Mexico	$2.17
Spain	$12.65
United States	$15.45

Source: The Universal Almanac

Each student in a class has taken five tests. The teacher allows the students to pick the mean, median, or mode for each set of scores. Which average should each student pick in order to have the highest average?

12. 100, 87, 81, 23, 19 _____

13. 90, 80, 74, 74, 72 _____

14. 80, 80, 70, 67, 68 _____

15. 75, 78, 77, 70, 70 _____

16. 100, 47, 45, 32, 31 _____

17. 86, 86, 77, 14, 12 _____

18. 79, 78, 77, 76, 85 _____

19. 86, 80, 79, 70, 70 _____

Practice

Gervase works after school and on weekends at a pet store, where he is paid $5 per hour. He used the following spreadsheet to keep track of the time he works and the money he earns.

	A	B	C	D	E
1	Day	Time In (PM)	Time Out (PM)	Hours Worked	Amount Earned
2	Monday	4	7		
3	Tuesday	4	7		
4	Thursday	4	8		
5	Saturday	1	9		
6			Total		

1. How can the value of cell D2 be calculated?

   _____

2. How can the value of cell E2 be calculated?

   _____

3. Write the formula to find the value of cell D6.

   _____

4. Write the formula to find the value of cell E6.

   _____

5. How many hours does Gervase work in a week?

   _____

6. How much does Gervase earn in a week?

   _____

7. Determine Gervase's weekly earnings if he receives a $1 per hour raise.

   _____

8. Determine Gervase's weekly earnings if he receives a $1 per hour raise and works 4 hours on Friday night.

   _____

9. Rosaria, Alphonse, John, and Nancy went together to buy a car for $6,000. John paid half as much as the other three paid. Rosaria paid one-third as much as the other three paid. Alphonse paid one-fourth as much as the other three paid. How much did each person pay? Use a spreadsheet to solve the problem.

   _____

■■■Practice

Use the circle graph for Exercises 1–3.

1. Which element is found in greatest quantity in the body?

   _____

2. What are the three elements named?

   _____

3. Why might there be a portion labeled "other"?

   _____

   _____

Major Elements Found In The Body

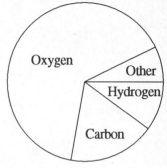

Use the bar graph for Exercises 4–6.

4. Which part of the world has the greatest number of operating nuclear reactors?

   _____

5. Which two parts of the world have the fewest number of active nuclear reactors?

   _____

6. Which part of the world has about twice as many nuclear reactors in operation as the Far East?

   _____

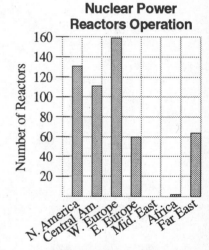

Use the line graph for Exercises 7–8.

7. What overall trend does the line graph show?

   _____

8. During which 10-year period did the percent of never-before married men decrease?

   _____

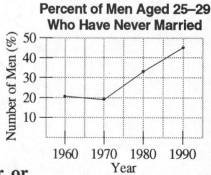

Circle A, B, C, or D. Which type of graph, circle, bar, or line, would be most appropriate to display the data?

9. The height of a child from age 1 to 6.

   A. Circle graph   **B.** Bar graph   **C.** Line graph   **D.** Any graph

© Prentice-Hall, Inc.

━━━━ **Practice**

Use the table below to answer Exercises 1-3.

All-time Favorite Sports Figures

Sports Figure	Number of Votes
Babe Ruth	29
Babe Didrikson Zaharias	22
Jackie Robinson	18
Billie Jean Moffitt King	17
Muhammed Ali	14
Jim Thorpe	13

Source: The Book of Lists #3, The People's Almanac

1. What would you label the horizontal axis for a bar graph of the information?

_____

2. To construct a bar graph, what interval would you use for the vertical axis?

_____

3. Construct a bar graph displaying the number of votes for favorite sports figures of all times.

Use the table below to answer Exercises 4 and 5.
Daily Use of Petroleum in the U.S.
(Millions of Barrels)

Year	Number
1950	6.5
1955	8.5
1960	9.8
1965	11.5
1970	14.7
1975	16.3
1980	17.1
1985	15.7
1990	16.9

Source: U.S. Dept. of Energy, Annual Energy Review

4. Construct either a bar graph or a line graph for the amount of petroleum used daily in the U.S.

5. What interval would you use for the vertical axis to construct the graph in Exercise 4?

6. Draw a bar graph to display the data in the table at the right.

Millions of Heads of Cattle Raised (1990)

Country	Number
India	197
Brazil	140
U.S.	98
China	77
Ethiopia	30

Source: The Universal Almanac

▬▬▬Practice

There are only two used car dealers in Auto City, Junkers and Clunkers. Monthly auto sales for January, February, and March are shown for Clunkers.

Clunker's Monthly Auto Sales	
January	15
February	14
March	13

1. Draw a bar graph that Junkers could use to show that Clunkers' business is really falling off.

2. Draw a line graph that Clunkers could use to show that business has been stable.

3. What is the actual decline in auto sales for Clunkers?

_____

4. Using data from the first three months of the year, can you determine if sales for the whole year will be bad? Explain.

_____

_____

_____

Use the line graph for Exercises 5-7.

5. What is wrong with the way the graph is drawn?

_____

_____

6. What impression does the graph try to present?

_____

_____

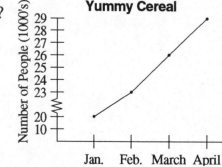

Number of People Who Prefer Yummy Cereal

7. Draw a graph that presents the information correctly.

Course 1 • *Chapter 1*

■■■■ Practice

Name each of the following. Use the diagram at the right.

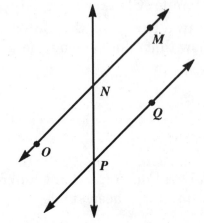

1. three collinear points

   _____

2. three noncollinear points

   _____

3. three segments

   _____

4. three rays

   _____

5. two lines that appear to be parallel

   _____

6. two pairs of intersecting lines

   _____

7. Draw four collinear points.

8. Draw five noncollinear points.

Complete each sentence with *sometimes, always,* or *never.*

9. Three points are _____ collinear.

10. Four points are _____ noncollinear.

11. A ray _____ has one endpoint.

12. A line _____ has an endpoint.

Name the segments that appear to be parallel.

13.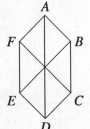

    _____

14.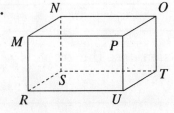

    _____

    _____

Practice

Use the diagram at the right.

1. Name three rays.

_____

2. Name three angles. Classify each
angle as acute, right, obtuse, or
straight.

_____

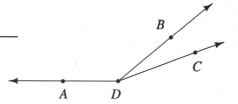

Without using your protractor, estimate the measure of each angle.
Choose the best estimate from 30°, 60°, 90°, 120°, 150°.

3. _____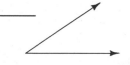

4. _____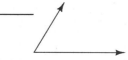

5. _____

6. _____

Use a protractor to draw an angle with each measure.

7. 88°

8. 65°

Use the diagram at the right.

9. Find the measure of ∠*MSN*, ∠*NSO*, ∠*OSP*,
∠*PSQ*, and ∠*QSR*.

10. List all of the obtuse angles shown.

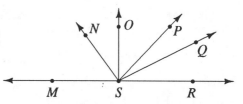

_____

11. List all of the right
angles shown.

12. List all the straight
angles shown.

13. List all the acute angles
shown.

_____   _____   _____

_____

_____

14. **Circle A, B, C, or D.** Which measure
is not a measure of one of the angles in
the figure shown at the right?

    A. 45°   **B.** 135°   **C.** 90°   **D.** 120°

Practice

Construct a segment congruent to each segment.

1.

2. J •————————————• K

Construct a segment twice as long as each segment.

3. C •————————• D

4.

Construct an angle congruent to each angle.

5.

6.

Construct an angle that has twice the measure of each angle.

7.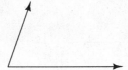

8.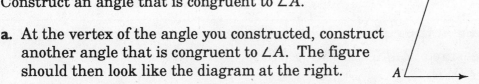

Construct a pentagon with sides of equal length as follows.

9. Construct an angle that is congruent to $\angle A$.

   a. At the vertex of the angle you constructed, construct
      another angle that is congruent to $\angle A$. The figure
      should then look like the diagram at the right.

   b. Continue constructing three more angles that are
      congruent to $\angle A$ so that all the angles have the same
      vertex. You should have a diagram like the one at
      the right.

   c. Mark off equal segments on each ray of the angles you
      constructed. Connect the endpoints of these segments.
      You should have a pentagon with sides of equal length.

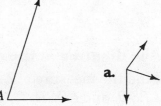

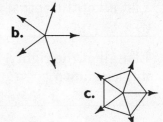

▰▰▰▰Practice

Use a centimeter ruler and protractor to measure the sides and angles of each triangle. Classify each triangle according to its angle measures and side lengths.

1.

2.

3.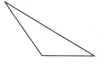

_____   _____   _____

Classify the triangle described as *scalene, isosceles,* or *equilateral*.

4. The side lengths are 8, 9, and 8.

_____

5. The side lengths are 3, 4, and 5.

_____

6. The side lengths are 15, 15, and 15.

_____

7. The side lengths are 4, 7, and 9.

_____

Classify the triangle described as *acute, right,* or *obtuse*.

8. The angle measures are 60°, 60°, and 60°.

_____

9. The angle measures are 25°, 14°, and 141°.

_____

10. The angle measures are 90°, 63°, and 27°.

_____

11. The angle measures are 90°, 89°, and 1°.

_____

If possible, sketch each triangle. If you cannot sketch a triangle, explain.

12. a right obtuse triangle

13. an acute equilateral triangle

14. an isosceles scalene triangle

_____   _____   _____
_____   _____   _____
_____   _____   _____
                                        _____

Practice

Classify each polygon.

1. _____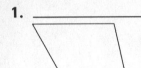

2. _____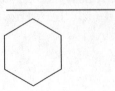

3. _____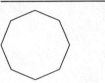

4. _____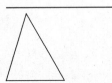

5. _____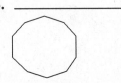

6. _____

Use the dot paper below to draw each polygon.

7. a quadrilateral with one right angle

8. a pentagon with no right angle

9. a hexagon with two right angles

 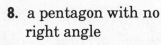 

10. Trace and cut out the following shapes. Rearrange the shapes to form a lowercase "t".

  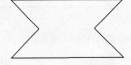

11. Trace and cut out the plus sign. Cut it into four equal pieces. Rearrange the pieces to form a square that has the same height and width as the plus sign.

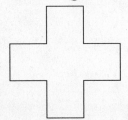

▄▄▄Practice

List the letters of all the polygons that have each name.

1. quadrilateral

    _____

2. parallelogram

    _____

3. rhombus

    _____

4. rectangle

    _____

5. square

    _____

6. trapezoid

    _____

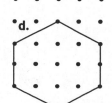
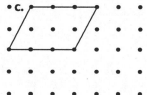
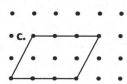

State the best name for each polygon shown above.

7. a   8. b   9. c   10. d

    _____   _____   _____   _____

11. e   12. f   13. g   14. h

    _____   _____   _____   _____

Sketch each quadrilateral.

15. a parallelogram that   16. a quadrilateral that   17. a rectangle
    is not a rectangle   is not a parallelogram

18. How many squares can you find in the figure?

    _____

19. Move four of the line segments from the large square so that three squares result.

Practice

Solve each problem using logical reasoning. Show all your work.

1. A local restaurant features a three-course meal. For the first course, you can choose from soup, salad, cottage cheese, or coleslaw. For the second course, you can choose from beef, pork, chicken, or a vegetarian pasta dish. For the third course, you can choose from sherbet, rice pudding, or gelatin. How many different meals could you choose if you choose one item from each course?

_____

2. In a sixth-grade class of 28 students, 23 like to watch basketball. Also, 15 like to watch baseball. Twelve in the class said they like to watch both sports. How many in the class do not like to watch either sport?

_____

Use any strategy to solve each problem. Show all your work.

3. Don has a pile of pennies. When he separates the pennies into stacks of two, he has one left over. When he separates the pennies into stacks of five, he has four left over. When he separates the pennies into stacks of seven, there are none left over. What is the least number of pennies that Don could have?

_____

4. Mara bought some flowers to plant in her garden. When she separated the plants into groups of three or five, she had one plant left over. When she separated the plants into groups of eight, she had none left over. What is the smallest number of plants that Mara could have bought?

_____

5. Rearrange these numbers so that the sum of the three numbers along each segment is 12.

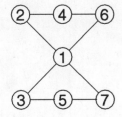

© Prentice-Hall, Inc.

■■■ Practice

State whether each figure appears to be congruent to the parallelogram at the right.

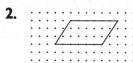

1.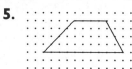

2.

3.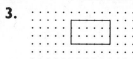

4.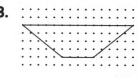

_____   _____   _____   _____

State whether each trapezoid appears to be similar to the trapezoid at the right.

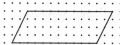

5.

6.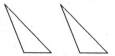

7.

8.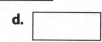

_____   _____   _____   _____

Tell whether the triangles appear to be *congruent*, *similar*, or *neither*.

9.

10.

11.

_____   _____   _____

12. List the pairs of figures that appear to be similar. _____

a. **b.** **c.** **d.**

e. **f.** **g.** **h.**

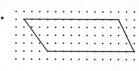

13. The figure below contains eight congruent triangles. Redraw the figure with four fewer segments, so that only four congruent triangles remain.

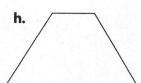

© Prentice-Hall, Inc.

▬▬▬*Practice*

Does the figure have line symmetry? If it does, draw all the lines of symmetry. If not, write *none*.

1.

2.

3.

4.

5.

6.

Complete each figure so that the line is a line of symmetry.

7.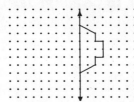

8.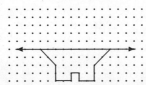

9.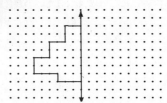

10.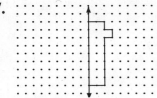

11.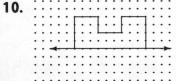

12.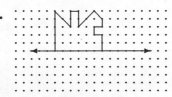

Can you find a line of symmetry for each word? If so, draw the line of symmetry.

13. BOX   14. TOOT   15. CHICO   16. MOM

17. Many logos such as the one at the right have both horizontal line symmetry and vertical line symmetry.

   a. Design another logo that has both horizontal and vertical line symmetry.

   b. Design another logo that has only horizontal line symmetry.

   c. Design another logo that has only vertical line symmetry.

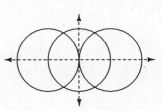

Practice

Name each of the following for circle O.

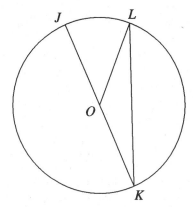

1. three radii

   _____

2. a diameter

   _____

3. two chords

   _____

4. two central angles

   _____

5. If the radius of a circle is 4 in., what is the diameter?

   _____

6. If the diameter of a circle is 15 cm, what is the radius?

   _____

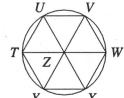

Circle A, B, C, or D. What is the measure of each angle?

7. ∠UZT

   A. 60°   **B.** 120°   **C.** 150°   **D.** 180°

8. ∠TZW

   A. 60°   **B.** 120°   **C.** 150°   **D.** 180°

9. ∠UZY

   A. 60°   **B.** 120°   **C.** 150°   **D.** 180°

10. ∠TYV

    A. 60°   **B.** 120°   **C.** 150°   **D.** 180°

11. A toy race car has a wheel with a diameter of 10 in. A larger car has a wheel with a diameter of 14 in. A designer plans to include 9 spokes from the center of each wheel. What will be the measure of the central angle formed by two consecutive spokes of the 10 in. wheel? of the 14 in. wheel? What can you conclude?

    _____

    _____

Practice

Trace and cut out several of each figure. Determine whether you can use the figure to form a tessellation.

1.
_____

2.
_____

3.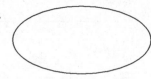
_____

4.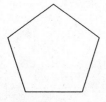
_____

5.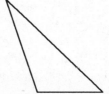
_____

6.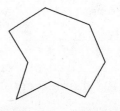
_____

Show how to use each set of figures to form a tessellation.

7.

8.

9.

10.

11. **Circle A, B, C, or D.** Which of the following could you use to tessellate the plane?

A.
B.
C.
D.

Practice

Draw a model for each decimal.

1. 0.4

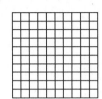

2. 0.72

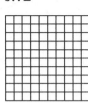

3. 0.10

Write each decimal in words.

4. 0.9

_____

5. 0.1

_____

6. 0.04

_____

7. 0.07

_____

8. 0.29

_____

9. 0.46

_____

10. 0.80

_____

11. 0.30

_____

12. 0.03

_____

Write a decimal for each model.

13.

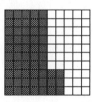

_____

14.

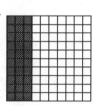

_____

15.

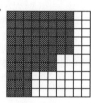

_____

Write a decimal for the given words.

16. three tenths

_____

17. fifty-two hundredths

_____

18. eight tenths

_____

19. two hundredths

_____

20. seventy-nine hundredths

21. forty hundredths

_____

Write the number in each problem as a decimal.

22. Five out of ten of Grandma Moses' children survived infancy.

_____

23. The amount of ozone necessary to protect Earth would make a layer on the surface that is sixteen hundredths of an inch thick.

_____

Practice

What is the value of the digit 7 in each number?

1. 0.7

2. 4.00712

3. 2.179

_____

_____

_____

4. 7.089

5. 348.92971

6. 72.14

_____

_____

_____

Write the words for each number in standard form.

7. 12.873

8. 8.0552

9. 1.0924

_____

_____

_____

_____

_____

_____

_____

_____

_____

10. 3.4700

11. 0.00065

12. 0.0049

_____

_____

_____

_____

_____

_____

_____

_____

_____

Write each number in expanded form.

13. 5.349

14. 0.7829

_____

_____

15. 8.495

16. fourteen and three tenths

_____

_____

17. ten and eleven thousandths

18. three and fifteen hundred-thousandths

_____

_____

19. Draw a model for two and thirty-seven hundredths.

   a. Write the number in expanded form._____

   b. In your model, how did you represent

      two? _____

   c. How many tenths and hundredths did

      you shade? _____

   d. Write the number in standard form.

      _____

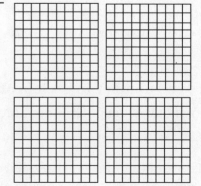

Practice

Compare. Use >, <, or =.

1. 0.62 ☐ 0.618   **2.** 9.8 ☐ 9.80   **3.** 1.006 ☐ 1.02   **4.** 41.3 ☐ 41.03

5. 2.01 ☐ 2.011   **6.** 1.400 ☐ 1.40   **7.** 5.079 ☐ 5.08   **8.** 12.96 ☐ 12.967

9. 15.8 ☐ 15.800   **10.** 7.98 ☐ 7.89   **11.** 8.02 ☐ 8.020   **12.** 5.693 ☐ 5.299

13. Graph 0.2, 0.6, and 0.5 on a number line.   **14.** Graph 0.26, 0.3, 0.5, 0.59, and 0.7 on a number line

15. Circle A, B, C, or D. Points X, Y, and Z are decimals graphed on a number line. Read statements I-IV. Which two statements give exactly the same information?

I. Y is greater than X and Z II. $X > Y$ and $X > Z$

III. $Y > Z$ and $Z > X$ IV. $Y > Z$ and $Y > X$

A. I and II   **B.** II and III   **C.** II and IV   **D.** I and IV

16. Draw a model to represent 0.67 and a model to represent 0.675.

   a. Which number is greater? _____

   b. How did the models show which number is greater?

   _____

17. Below are models that represent numbers.

   a. Write the number that each model represents.

   _____

   b. Order the decimals from least to greatest.

   _____

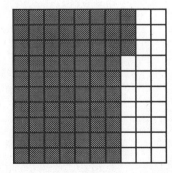   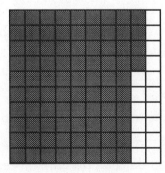   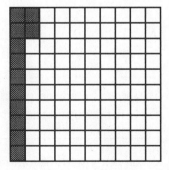

Practice

Solve by using a simpler problem.

1. At 8:00 P.M., there are 243 people in line for a ride at an amusement park. Every 12 minutes starting at 8 P.M., 42 people are able to enter the ride. A boy gets in line at 8:00. Will he get to ride before the ride shuts down at 9:00 P.M.? Explain.

   _____

   _____

2. The astronauts who landed on the moon brought back about 842 pounds of moon rocks. Dividing the cost of these moon flights by the weight of the rocks, it is estimated that the rocks cost $3,000,000 per ounce. What was the approximate cost of these moon flights? _____

3. While an adult is asleep, his or her heart can pump about 80 gal of blood per hour. About how many gallons of blood will the heart pump during a week of sleep if an adult sleeps 7 h each night? _____

Use any strategy to solve each problem. Show all your work.

4. The Language Club includes students who are enrolled in Latin, German, Spanish, or French. Each person, including John, is enrolled in only one foreign language. Christine does not speak French. Judy is enrolled in German or Latin. Pepe is enrolled in Latin or Spanish. Christine and the person taking Spanish often walk to school together. Christine and the person who is taking German are best friends. Who is enrolled in which course?

   _____

   _____

5. What is the sum of all odd numbers from 101 to 200?

   _____

6. A small humming bird beats its wings 70 times/s. How many times will it beat its wings in 8 h?

   _____

7. It takes the sound of thunder five seconds to travel one mile. How far away is the thunder if it takes 45 s to reach you?

   _____

8. A company with 628 employees is taking all the employees to see a baseball game. The company will hire buses. If each bus holds 34 passengers, will 15 buses be enough? _____

Practice

Write the sum or difference represented by the models.

1. 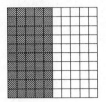 +

_____

2.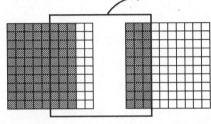

Add or subtract. You may use models.

3. 3.9 + 2.6	**4.** 7.1 − 0.8	**5.** 0.26 + 0.53	**6.** 0.54 − 0.21
7. 1.2 + 0.91	**8.** 3.92 +0.63	**9.** 1.52 − 0.27	**10.** 0.93 − 0.57
11. 1.2 + 4.9	**12.** 0.83 −0.24	**13.** 4.1 + 5.7	**14.** 0.81 +0.56
15. 0.26 − 0.07	**16.** 0.9 + 0.8	**17.** 2.07 − 1.48	**18.** 1.59 +2.41
19. 0.96 − 0.47	**20.** 0.27 +0.85	**21.** 1.96 −0.97	**22.** 0.52 +0.78

Practice

Round to the place of the underlined digit.

1. 1.1<u>09</u>

2. 2.<u>3</u>57

3. 4.87<u>7</u>2

4. 5.8<u>0</u>45

Round to the nearest dollar to estimate.

5. $8.92
   + 5.19

6. $32.18
   − 14.09

7. $29.99
   + 15.29

8. $26.49
   − 13.99

9. $21.95
   − 7.15

10. $83.49
    − 56.13

11. $1.87
    + 5.28

12. $43.87
    + 26.15

13. $15.49
    + 12.86

14. $23.57
    − 18.99

15. $49.17
    − 5.88

16. $19.95
    + 21.36

Use front-end estimation to find each sum. Show how you estimated.

17. $2.59 + $3.76 + 2.41 _____

18. $8.19 + $2.46 + $3.57 _____

19. $3.61 + $2.17 + $5.84 _____

20. $9.14 + $8.72 + $5.63 _____

Circle A, B, C, or D. Choose the sum that is most appropriate for the given range of low and high estimates.

21. low: 11; high: 14

A. 2.89 + 3.51 + 6.62
B. 1.27 + 1.89 + 2.34
C. 3.45 + 4.62 + 7.32
D. 2.01 + 3.22 + 4.56

22. low: 24; high: 25

A. 9.83 + 8.16 + 7.58
B. 7.08 + 8.91 + 9.23
C. 8.12 + 7.43 + 6.27
D. 10.06 + 6.94 + 8.58

23. low: 56; high: 58

A. 14.78 + 23.92 + 16.37
B. 34.96 + 2.43 + 8.74
C. 16.88 + 17.12 + 25.94
D. 15.78 + 23.41 + 18.49

24. low: 52; high: 55

A. 14.78 + 21.05 + 14.71
B. 23.86 + 15.93 + 18.92
C. 15.96 + 18.72 + 19.41
D. 42.56 + 8.32 + 5.64

25. Dom has $12. He wants to buy 3 audio cassette tapes that cost $5.79 each and a notebook that costs $.89. Does Dom have enough money? Explain.

_____

_____

Practice

First estimate. Then find the sum or difference.

1. $0.6 + 5.8$

2. $2.1 + 3.4$

3. $3.4 - 0.972$

4. $3.1 - 2.076$

_____

_____

_____

_____

5. $8.13 - 2.716$

6. $5.91 + 2.38$

7. $3.086 + 6.152$

8. $4.7 - 1.9$

_____

_____

_____

_____

9. $9.3 - 3.9$

10. $5.2 - 1.86$

11. $15.98 + 26.37$

12. $9.27 + 15.006$

_____

_____

_____

_____

13. $5.9 - 2.803$

14. $15.7 - 8.923$

15. $4.19 - 2.016$

16. $14.75 - 6.9264$

_____

_____

_____

_____

17. $5.1 + 4.83 + 9.002$

18. $3 + 4.02 + 8.6$

19. $4.7 + 5.26 + 8.931$

_____

_____

_____

20. $5.68 + 2.03 + 5.091$

21. $3.86 + 9.604 + 5.793$

22. $14.7 + 23.92 + 15.872$

_____

_____

_____

Use the table at the right for Exercises 23–25.

23. Find the sum of the decimals given in the chart. What is the meaning of this sum?

_____

_____

24. What part of the hourly work force is from ages 25-44? _____

25. Which three age groups combined represent about one-fourth of the hourly work force?

_____

_____

Ages of Workers Earning Hourly Pay

Age of Workers	Part of Work Force
16-19	0.08
20-24	0.15
25-34	0.29
35-44	0.24
45-54	0.14
55-64	0.08
65 & over	0.02

Source: Bureau of Labor Statistics, U.S. Dept. of Labor

26. At the grocery store, you need to buy a gallon of milk that costs $1.59, a pound of spaghetti that costs $.77, apples that cost $.89 a bag, green beans that cost $.59 a can, and juice that costs $.89 a bottle. You have $5.00.

a. Estimate whether you have enough money. Explain how you estimated. _____

b. Check your answer by addition. How much did the groceries cost? _____

Practice

Find the missing entries in the savings account record.

Date	Balance (Start of Day)	Withdrawal	Deposit	Interest	Balance (End of Day)
March 3	1.		25.13		106.92
March 8	2.	3.			4.
March 10	48.75		76.89		5.
March 18	6.		58.17		7.
March 24	8.		53.28		9.
March 30	10.	30.00			11.
March 31	12.			1.06	13.

Mr. Ramirez just began a new job as an accountant for the Top-Notch Manufacturing Company. His first assignment is to make a balance sheet and include all the deposits and withdrawals made the month before he began work. Show what Mr. Ramirez's balance sheet would look like.

Withdrawal
10/1 $549.87

Deposit
10/20 $756.87

Withdrawal
10/3 201.47

Deposit
10/6 $589.90

Withdrawal
10/10 $96.99

Withdrawal
10/5 $186.19

Withdrawal
10/8 $256.83

	Date	Deposit	Withdrawal	Balance $1,274.98
14.	10/1			
15.	10/3			
16.	10/5			
17.	10/6			
18.	10/8			
19.	10/10			
20.	10/20			

Practice

Measure each segment in millimeters.

1. ————————————

2. ———————

3. ——————————————

4. ——————————

Find the perimeter of each figure.

5. _____

6. _____

7. _____

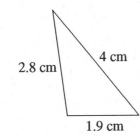

2.8 cm 4 cm 1.9 cm

2.2 cm 3.7 cm

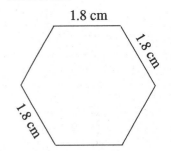

1.8 cm 1.8 cm 1.8 cm

8. Draw a figure that has a perimeter of 14 cm.

Circle A, B, C, or D. Is each measurement reasonable? If not, choose a reasonable measurement.

9. Your friend is 1,500 mm tall.
   - **A.** 1.5 mm
   - **B.** 1,500 cm
   - **C.** 1.5 km
   - **D.** reasonable

10. Your desk is about 50 mm wide.
    - **A.** 50 m
    - **B.** 50 cm
    - **C.** 5 m
    - **D.** reasonable

11. A tree is about 20 km tall.
    - **A.** 20 m
    - **B.** 2 km
    - **C.** 20 cm
    - **D.** reasonable

12. An envelope is about 24 cm long.
    - **A.** 2.4 cm
    - **B.** 24 mm
    - **C.** 2.4 m
    - **D.** reasonable

Circle A, B, C, or D. What unit would you use to measure each item?

13. The height of an office building
    - **A.** km
    - **B.** m
    - **C.** cm
    - **D.** mm

14. The width of a page of a text
    - **A.** km
    - **B.** m
    - **C.** cm
    - **D.** mm

15. The length of an ant
    - **A.** km
    - **B.** m
    - **C.** cm
    - **D.** mm

16. The depth of an ocean
    - **A.** km
    - **B.** m
    - **C.** cm
    - **D.** mm

Practice

Clark is trying to plan his day out for Saturday. He estimates each activity will take the following times.

Make a schedule for Clark's day, if he wakes up at 7:00 A.M. Assume all his activities are done in the given order.

	Activity	Amount of Time	Time of Day
1.	Get up, eat breakfast	30 min	
2.	Mow lawn	1 h	
3.	Rake yard	2 h	
4.	Wash, wax car	45 min	
5.	Walk dog	15 min	
6.	Clean room	45 min	
7.	Eat lunch	30 min	
8.	Shop for school clothes	1 h 30 min	
9.	Read book	45 min	
10.	Do homework	1 h 15 min	
11.	Baby-sit brother	2 h	
12.	Eat supper	45 min	
13.	Get ready for party	30 min	
14.	Ride to party	20 min	
15.	Party	2 h	
16.	Ride home	20 min	

Weekdays — Westbound

Local Stop	Central Court	River Grove
6:03 A.M.	6:12 A.M.	6:24 A.M.
6:33	6:42	6:54
7:03	7:12	7:24
7:33	7:42	7:54
8:03	8:12	8:24
8:38	8:47	8:59
9:03	9:12	9:24
9:34	9:43	9:55
10:34	10:43	10:55
11:34	11:43	11:55
12:34 P.M.	12:43 P.M.	12:55 P.M.
1:34	1:43	1:55

Weekdays — Eastbound

River Grove	Central Court	Local Stop
6:18 A.M.	6:32 A.M.	6:40 A.M.
6:42	6:56	7:04
7:16	7:32	7:40
7:51	8:07	8:15
8:16	8:32	8:40
8:47	9:01	9:08
9:47	10:01	10:08
10:47	11:01	11:08
11:47	12:01 P.M.	12:08 P.M.
12:47 P.M.	1:01	1:08
1:47	2:01	2:08
2:47	3:01	3:08

17. Morgan has errands to do. It takes him 12 min to walk to the bus station. He takes the 9:03 A.M. bus to Central Court. At Central Court he spends 20 min shopping and then takes the bus to River Grove to pick up his new eyeglasses. This takes 25 min. Then he takes the bus to his local stop and walks home. Morgan always takes the first bus he can catch at each stop.

a. What time should Morgan leave home?_____

b. What time will Morgan return home? _____

© Prentice-Hall, Inc.

Practice

Round each factor to the nearest whole number to estimate the product.

1. 0.97×13.21 _____

2. 11.9×4.76 _____

3. 14.7×2.2 _____

4. 18.95×0.76 _____

5. 28.02×1.94 _____

6. 11.93×1.63 _____

7. 43.75×3.17 _____

8. 5.02×3.16 _____

9. 9.04×8.71 _____

10. 17.41×8.04 _____

11. 8.59×0.81 _____

12. 21.7×2.03 _____

13. 8.07×9.63 _____

14. 0.96×15.41 _____

15. 5.21×6.78 _____

Use compatible numbers to estimate.

16. 38.9×19.7 _____

17. $18.47 \div 5.96$ _____

18. 21.19×9.4 _____

19. $38.4 \div 3.6$ _____

20. $76.3 \div 15.1$ _____

21. 11.9×9.8 _____

22. $49.1 \div 15.6$ _____

23. 21.8×6.31 _____

24. $18.6 \div 2.8$ _____

25. 18.9×4.7 _____

26. $63.7 \div 7.6$ _____

27. 24.6×3.8 _____

28. $19.7 \div 4.1$ _____

29. 16.1×7.42 _____

30. $82.3 \div 8.76$ _____

Tim went shopping and spent $31.79 at each of 3 stores.

31. Use compatible numbers to estimate how much Tim spent altogether. _____

32. Estimate how much Tim spent by rounding.

_____

33. Which estimate is closer to the amount Tim actually spent?

_____

Practice

Use the table below for Exercises 1–11.

1991-1992 NBA Players

Player	Games Played	Total Points	Average
Michael Jordan	80	2,404	30.1
Patrick Ewing	82	1,870	22.8
David Robinson	68	1,578	23.2
Hakeem Olajuwon	70	1,510	21.6
Scottie Pippen	82	1,720	21.0
Reggie Lewis	82	1,703	20.8
Jeff Malone	81	1,639	20.2

Source: The 1993 Information Please Almanac

1. How many points did David Robinson average for 1991-1992?

_____

2. Who averaged 21.0 points per game in 1991-1992?

_____

3. Who played the fewest games in 1991-1992?

_____

4. Who scored the most total points for 1991-1992?

_____

5. Who played 81 games in 1991-1992? _____

6. Who scored the fewest number of points in 1991-1992?

_____

7. If David Robinson had played 82 games, without changing his average points per game, what would have been his total points scored? _____

8. If Michael Jordan had played two more games in which he scored 45 points and 36 points, what would have been his average? _____

9. How many points would Hakeem Olajuwon have had to score in 12 games in order to raise his average to 25.0 points?

_____

10. If Hakeem Olajuwon had raised his average to 25.0 points per game, what would his average have had to be for the additional 12 games? _____

11. If only one player had played all of the games listed and scored all of the points, what would that player's average have been?

_____

Practice

Which operation would you perform first?

1. $4 + 6 \times 9$

_____

2. $(7.1 - 5.6) \times 3$

_____

3. $14 \div 2 \times 3$

_____

4. $18 - 5 + 3$

_____

5. $5.3 \times 2.1 + 6.3$

_____

6. $5.3 \times (2.1 + 6.3)$

_____

7. $(9 + 14) - 8 \div 2$

_____

8. $\frac{27}{4} \times 13 + 6$

_____

9. $18 - 3 \times 6$

_____

Evaluate.

10. $8 - 3 \times 1 + 5$

_____

11. $(4.3 - 2.6) \times 5$

_____

12. $14 \times 6 \div 3$

_____

13. $10 \div (6.3 - 4.3)$

_____

14. $9 \times (3 \times 5)$

_____

15. $7 \times (8 + 6)$

_____

16. $15 - (2.6 + 3.1)$

_____

17. $(12 - 9) \times (6 + 1)$

_____

18. $(9 - 3) \times 2$

_____

19. $8 - 3 \times 2 + 7$

_____

20. $(9 - 4) \times 6$

_____

21. $14 - (2.6 + 3.4)$

_____

Evaluate using mental math.

22. $3 + 5 \times 0$

_____

23. $(11 - 8) \times 4 + 1$

_____

24. $(8.6 - 4.2) \times 1$

_____

25. $27 \div 9 - (7.3 - 6.3)$

_____

26. $(15.3 - 8.9) \times 0$

_____

27. $(15 - 8) \times 7 - 4$

_____

Insert parentheses so that a true statement will be formed.

28. $6 + 7 \times 4 - 2 = 26$

_____

29. $14 - 5 \div 3 = 3$

_____

30. $27 \div 4 + 5 - 1 = 2$

_____

31. Mr. Piña bought a bag of apples for $1.59, a dozen eggs for $.79, a gallon of milk for $1.79, and a loaf of bread for $1.20. Estimate Mr. Piña's grocery bill.

_____

Course 1 • Chapter 4

■■■■Practice

Write two expressions to describe the total area. Then find the total area.

1.
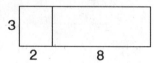
3
2   8

2.
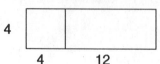
4
4   12

3.
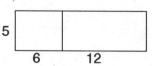
5
6   12

_____   _____   _____

_____   _____   _____

Fill in the missing numbers.

4. $8 \times (9 + 4) = (\boxed{} \times 9) + (8 \times \boxed{})$ 5. $(4 \times 7) + (4 \times 5) = 4 \times (\boxed{} + 5)$

6. $9 \times (7 - 1) = (9 \times \boxed{}) - (\boxed{} \times 1)$ 7. $(5 \times 7) + (5 \times 6) = \boxed{} \times (7 + 6)$

8. $3 \times (7 + 9) = (\boxed{} \times 7) + (3 \times \boxed{})$ 9. $8 \times (9 - 6) = (8 \times \boxed{}) - (\boxed{} \times 6)$

Use the distributive property to evaluate.

10. 7×53 11. 8×97 12. 5×402

_____   _____   _____

13. 8×113 14. 9×213 15. 7×49

_____   _____   _____

Use the order of operations and the distributive property to evaluate.

16. $9 \times (5 + 3) \times 4 - 6$ 17. $(8 + 7) \times 3 \times 2$ 18. $5 \times 7 \times 3 + (5 - 4)$

_____   _____   _____

19. $6 \times (8 - 3) + 9 \times 4$ 20. $7 \times (8 - 2) \times 4 + 9$ 21. $(8 + 6) \times 3 \times 9$

_____   _____   _____

Insert parentheses into each equation so that a true statement is formed.

22. $8 + 6 \div 2 + 9 - 3 \times 2 = 19$ 23. $6 \times 3 + 4 - 9 + 7 = 26$

_____   _____

24. $9 - 4 \times 6 - 8 + 1 = 21$ 25. $8 + 7 \div 5 + 2 + 7 \times 3 = 30$

_____   _____

© Prentice-Hall, Inc.

Name _____ Class _____ Date _____

Practice   *For use after 4–5*

Write a multiplication sentence to describe the model.

1.

2.

3.

4.

5.

Draw a model to find each product.

6. 0.4×0.4 **7.** 0.6×0.9 **8.** 0.8×0.7

9. 3×0.5 **10.** 2×0.9

Write the multiplication problem you could use to model each situation.

11. A pen costs $.59. How much would a dozen pens cost?

_____

12. A mint costs $.02. How much would a roll of 10 mints cost?

_____

13. A bottle of juice has a deposit of $.10 on the bottle. How much deposit would there be on 8 bottles? _____

14. An orange costs $.09. How much would 2 dozen oranges cost?

_____

© Prentice-Hall, Inc.

77   Course 1 • *Chapter 4*

▬▬■Practice

Place a decimal point in each product.

1. $4.3 \times 2.9 = 1247$

2. $0.279 \times 53 = 14787$

3. $4.09 \times 3.96 = 161964$

_____

_____

_____

4. $5.90 \times 6.3 = 3717$

5. $0.74 \times 83 = 6142$

6. $2.06 \times 15.9 = 32754$

_____

_____

_____

Find each product.

7. 8.7×100

8. 43.59×0.1

9. 5.97×10

_____

_____

_____

10. 246×0.01

11. 726×0.1

12. 5.23×100

_____

_____

_____

Find each product.

13.
$$\begin{array}{r} 5.342 \\ \times \quad 13 \\ \hline \end{array}$$

14.
$$\begin{array}{r} 0.19 \\ \times 0.05 \\ \hline \end{array}$$

15.
$$\begin{array}{r} 6.4 \\ \times 0.09 \\ \hline \end{array}$$

16.
$$\begin{array}{r} 240 \\ \times 0.02 \\ \hline \end{array}$$

17.
$$\begin{array}{r} 43.79 \\ \times \quad 42 \\ \hline \end{array}$$

18.
$$\begin{array}{r} 0.72 \\ \times 0.43 \\ \hline \end{array}$$

19.
$$\begin{array}{r} 6.72 \\ \times \quad 83 \\ \hline \end{array}$$

20.
$$\begin{array}{r} 0.27 \\ \times \quad 8.1 \\ \hline \end{array}$$

21.
$$\begin{array}{r} 5.96 \\ \times 0.08 \\ \hline \end{array}$$

22.
$$\begin{array}{r} 421 \\ \times 0.07 \\ \hline \end{array}$$

23.
$$\begin{array}{r} 9.87 \\ \times 5.63 \\ \hline \end{array}$$

24.
$$\begin{array}{r} 1.09 \\ \times 2.14 \\ \hline \end{array}$$

25.
$$\begin{array}{r} 8.76 \\ \times \quad 29 \\ \hline \end{array}$$

26.
$$\begin{array}{r} 42.7 \\ \times \quad 8.9 \\ \hline \end{array}$$

27.
$$\begin{array}{r} 4.03 \\ \times 0.09 \\ \hline \end{array}$$

28.
$$\begin{array}{r} 0.25 \\ \times 0.78 \\ \hline \end{array}$$

Write a digit in each space so that a true multiplication problem results. Place a decimal point in each product. No digit may be repeated. Use numbers 1–9.

29.

☐ ☐ . ☐
×   ☐ . ☐
─────────
4 ☐ ☐ ☐

30.

☐ ☐ . ☐
×   ☐ . ☐
─────────
☐ ☐   5 ☐

◼︎◼︎◼︎Practice

Solve if possible. If not, tell what information is needed.

1. The electrician charged Audun for a wiring job. The rates were $48/h, plus $23.56 for parts. What was the total amount Audun was charged?

   _____

2. A horse measured 12.6 hands in height. If a hand is about 4 in., what was the horse's height in inches?

   _____

3. Jamila works eight hours a week, for $4.55/h. How many weeks will she have to work in order to buy a stereo system that costs $492?

   _____

4. Kosey's school sold 397 tickets for a fun night and collected $893.25. If expenses came to $247.93, how much profit did the school make?

   _____

5. The Picnic Committee split up posters to be distributed to local merchants. If each committee member took 12 posters, how many merchants can display a poster about the picnic?

   _____

6. Rashida bought some boxes of greeting cards. One type cost $5.98 a box. Another type cost $7.29 a box. Rashida bought 15 boxes, and spent $97.56 total. How many boxes of each type did she buy?

   _____

7. Herman's salary increased each year according to the chart at the right. Assuming that the rate of increase for years 5 and 6 is the same as in all previous years, how much will he make during year 6?

Year	Amount
1	$1,000
2	$1,250
3	$1,562.50
4	$1,953.13

   _____

8. Jodi has some quarters and dimes. How many possible amounts of money could she have?

   _____

▰▰▰▰*Practice*

Complete each sentence.

1.

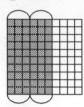

$\boxed{} \div 0.3 = 2$

2.

$0.4 \div 0.04 = \boxed{}$

3.

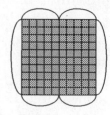

$1 \div \boxed{} = 2$

4.

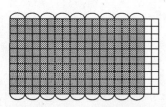

$\boxed{} \div 0.2 = 9$

5.

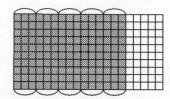

$1.5 \div \boxed{} = 5$

Draw a model to find each quotient.

6. $0.4 \div 0.08$ ____

7. $0.8 \div 0.4$ ____

8. $0.9 \div 0.15$ ____

9. $1.5 \div 0.75$ ____

10. $1.2 \div 0.12$ ____

Practice

Find each quotient.

1. $1.8 \div 6$

2. $16\overline{)3.2}$

3. $17\overline{)5.1}$

4. $9\overline{)21.6}$

5. $0.4\overline{)1.08}$

6. $0.68 \div 0.2$

7. $0.7\overline{)3.57}$

8. $0.6\overline{)5.88}$

9. $0.02\overline{)0.06}$

10. $0.09\overline{)0.108}$

11. $0.04\overline{)0.024}$

12. $0.07\overline{)0.3304}$

13. $11.18 \div 4.3$

14. $5.7\overline{)24.225}$

15. $3.6\overline{)18.072}$

16. $7.1\overline{)63.19}$

17. $5.2\overline{)43.68}$

18. $9.3\overline{)49.29}$

19. $65.026 \div 8.2$

20. $14.82 \div 5.7$

21. $5.3\overline{)2.279}$

22. $9.1\overline{)6.552}$

23. $4.042 \div 8.6$

24. $2.9\overline{)2.175}$

Choose a calculator, pencil and paper, or mental math to solve.

25. A package of 25 mechanical pencils cost $5.75. How much does each pencil cost? _____

26. A sales clerk is placing books side by side on a shelf. She has 12 copies of the same book. If the books cover 27.6 in. of the shelf, how thick is each book? _____

27. A car traveled 234.3 miles on 11 gallons of gas. How many miles per gallon did the car average? _____

28. Mr. Garza spent $80.73 on 9 cassette tapes. If they all cost the same amount, how much did each cassette tape cost?

_____

Practice

Choose a calculator, paper and pencil, estimation, or mental math. If necessary, round your answer to the nearest tenth.

1. How much more did an item cost in 1990 than in 1950?

   _____

2. How many times greater is the price of the item in 1990 than in 1950? _____

3. How much more did an item cost in 1980 than in 1950?

   _____

4. How many times greater is the price of the item in 1980 than in 1960? _____

5. How much less did an item cost in 1960 than in 1970?

   _____

6. How many times greater is the price of an item in 1990 than in 1970? _____

The table shows how much money different companies spent on advertising their products in 1990 and in 1991.

Company	Amount (in millions of dollars)	
	1990	1991
Sears, Roebuck & Co.	$1,432.1	$462.3
K Mart Corp.	$561.4	$186.5
Quaker Oats Co.	$357.8	$111.7
J.C. Penny Co.	$407.5	$105.2
H.J. Heinz Co.	$342.3	$77.1
Delta Airlines	$116.0	$123.4

Source: Leading National Advertisers, Inc.

7. What company had the largest drop in dollar amount spent on advertising from 1990 to 1991?

   _____

8. What company spent more on advertising in 1991 than it spent in 1990?

   _____

Practice

Find the next three terms in each number pattern. Write a rule to describe each number pattern.

1. 4, 7, 10, 13, ▦, ▦, ▦

_____

_____

2. 2, 4, 8, 16, ▦, ▦, ▦

_____

_____

3. $\frac{1}{3}$, $\frac{2}{3}$, 1, $1\frac{1}{3}$, ▦, ▦, ▦

_____

_____

4. 8, 11, 14, 17, ▦, ▦, ▦

_____

_____

5. 200, 100, 50, 25, ▦, ▦, ▦

_____

_____

6. 6,000, 600, 60, 6, ▦, ▦, ▦

_____

_____

7. Sketch the next two designs in the pattern.

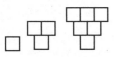

8. Sketch the next two designs in the pattern.

Circle A, B, C, or D. Which number is missing in each sequence?

9. 9, 16, 25, _____, 49

    A. 34   **B.** 42   **C.** 36   **D.** 40

10. $\frac{1}{4}$, $\frac{4}{9}$, $\frac{9}{16}$, _____, $\frac{25}{36}$

    A. $\frac{16}{32}$ **B.** $\frac{16}{25}$ **C.** $\frac{16}{49}$ **D.** $\frac{15}{28}$

11. 4, 5, 7, 10, _____, 19

    A. 15   **B.** 16   **C.** 17   **D.** 14

12. 3, 6, 18, 72, _____, 2,160

    A. 360   **B.** 350   **C.** 500   **D.** 1,116

Practice

Use Napier's rods to find each product.

1. 42×6 _____

2. 93×5 _____

3. 153×7 _____

4. 851×7 _____

5. 428×9 _____

6. $5{,}163 \times 7$ _____

7. $2{,}193 \times 4$ _____

8. $3{,}451 \times 6$ _____

9. $5{,}206 \times 8$ _____

10. $14{,}356 \times 7$ _____

11. $21{,}503 \times 8$ _____

12. $29{,}705 \times 4$ _____

13. $7{,}984 \times 6$ _____

14. $50{,}247 \times 9$ _____

15. $27{,}840 \times 3$ _____

16. $104{,}782 \times 9$ _____

17. The Widget Company manufactures 643 widgets each day. The profit on each widget is $6.00. How much profit does the Widget Company make in one day? _____

18. The Best Video Rental store rents 23 video tapes each hour. If the store is open 11 h, how many tapes does it rent in a day? _____

Write the product in each square. Draw a path from start to finish. You must always move to an adjacent square. You may move across, down, or diagonally, but you may only move to a square that has a product greater than the product in your current square.

Start

2×3 ___	4×1 ___	5×1 ___	2×5 ___	4×6 ___	7×8 ___
2×2 ___	3×4 ___	2×7 ___	3×3 ___	4×12 ___	8×8 ___
3×2 ___	3×1 ___	2×6 ___	3×5 ___	4×3 ___	5×7 ___
5×13 ___	4×7 ___	3×14 ___	3×7 ___	4×6 ___	3×6 ___
7×10 ___	5×17 ___	4×8 ___	5×6 ___	13×3 ___	3×7 ___
8×9 ___	6×4 ___	7×3 ___	9×4 ___	7×4 ___	9×9 ___
8×12 ___	5×8 ___	2×19 ___	8×5 ___	9×6 ___	7×8 ___

Finish

Practice

Choose a calculator, mental math, or paper and pencil to evaluate.

1. 9^2 **2.** 6^4 **3.** 5^3 **4.** 7^3

_____   _____   _____   _____

5. $156 + (256 \div 8^2)$ **6.** $32 + 64 + 2^3$ **7.** $53 + 64 \div 2^3$ **8.** $1{,}280 - 5 \times 6^2$

_____   _____   _____   _____

9. $7^3 - 3 \times 6 \div 2$ **10.** $17^2 - 8 \times 3$ **11.** $167 + (13 - 4)^3$ **12.** $(4 + 3)^2 - 17$

_____   _____   _____   _____

13. $8^3 - 5 \times 18 \div 3$ **14.** $5^2 \times 3 - 40$ **15.** $(9 + 3)^3$ **16.** $(24 - 16)^4$

_____   _____   _____   _____

Find each answer to complete the puzzle.

Across
1. $(3 \times 4)^2$
3. $60 \div (8 + 7) + 11$
4. $2^2 \times 5^2 + 106$
5. $4 + 7 \times 2^3$
6. $7^2 + 4$
9. $48 \div 4 \times 5 - 2 \times 5$
10. $(4 + 3) \times (2 + 1)$
12. $12 \times (30 + 37)$
13. $5 \times (9 + 4) + 362 \div 2$
14. $29 \times 18 \div 9$

Down
1. $8 \times (5 + 4) \div 6$
2. $700 \times (2 + 4) \div (17 - 7)$
3. $11 \times (18 - 3)$
5. $60 + (5 \times 4^3) + 2^2 \times 55$
7. $7^2 - 7 \times 2$
8. $(4^2 - 4) \times 10$
9. $2^4 \times 2^5$
11. $(3 + 2) \times (6^2 - 7)$
12. $3^4 + 405 \div 81$

■■■■■Practice

Choose a variable and write a variable expression for each model.

1.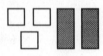

_____

2.

_____

3.

_____

Choose a calculator, mental math, or paper and pencil to evaluate.

4. $56 \div b$ for $b = 7$

_____

5. $3m$ for $m = 9$

_____

6. $8n$ for $n = 9$

_____

7. $4y + 6$ for $y = 18$

_____

8. $v^2 + 16$ for $v = 9$

_____

9. $2t - 8$ for $t = 21$

_____

10. $(4e)^2$ for $e = 5$

_____

11. $5gh$ for $g = 1.3$ and $h = 2.4$

_____

12. $3pq$ for $p = 1.3$ and $q = 5$

_____

13. $(7v)^2 + 18$ for $v = 11$

_____

14. $9r^2 + 16$ for $r = 8$

_____

15. $4vw$ for $v = 2.6$ and $w = 5.3$

_____

Use the table at the right to answer Exercises 16–17.

16. Find the time in each city when it is 4:00 P.M. in New York City.

_____

_____

_____

17. Find the time in each city when it is 10:00 A.M. in New York City.

_____

_____

City	International Time
New York	12:00 P.M.
Baghdad	8:00 P.M.
Chicago	11:00 A.M.
Dublin	5:00 P.M.
Melbourne	3:00 A.M.
Rio de Janeiro	2:00 P.M.
Vienna	6:00 P.M.

▬▬▬Practice

Use any strategy to solve each problem. Show all your work.

1. Find two numbers with a product of 72 and a sum of 17.

   _____

2. Juana is one year younger than her husband, Leo. The product of their ages is 650. How old is each?

   _____

3. A carpenter charges a basic fee of $25, plus $22/h. How much will she charge Ms. Lin if she works for 18 h?

   _____

4. The product of two numbers is 442. The sum of the two numbers is 43. Find the two numbers.

   _____

5. There are 42 students who signed up for youth camp and 56 students who signed up for family camp. There are 15 students who are signed up for both camps. What is the total number of students that are signed up for camp?

   _____

6. A radio station held a contest to give away concert tickets. On the first day, the first caller won. On the second day, the second caller won. On the third day, the fourth caller won. On the fourth day, the seventh caller won. Assuming that this pattern continued, did the thirtieth caller ever win?

   _____

7. Marquetta charged the Lees a basic fee of $35, plus $25/h for repairing their washing machine. What did the Lees pay if it took Marquetta 2.5 h to finish the job?

   _____

8. Sketch the next three drawings in the pattern.

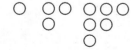

▰▰▰ Practice

Write two word phrases for each variable expression.

1. $5m$

2. $8 + b$

3. $15\,q$

_____

_____

_____

4. $c - 10$

5. $18 \div a$

6. $27 - m$

_____

_____

_____

7. $v \div 21$

8. $8r$

9. $t + 17$

_____

_____

_____

Write a variable expression for each word phrase. Choose an appropriate variable to represent an unknown quantity.

10. nine less than t

11. eleven more than a number

12. 700 divided by a number

_____

_____

_____

13. two times the number of windows

14. b divided by seven

15. a number more than 81

_____

_____

_____

16. twelve times the number of muffin pans

17. $15 times the number of hours

18. 8 less than a number

_____

_____

_____

Circle A, B, C, or D.

19. Which variable expression describes the area of the shaded region?

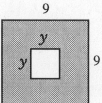

   A. $81 + y^2$ **C.** $81 - y^2$

   B. $y^2 - 81$ **D.** $18 - 2y$

20. Nadine has $1,293.76 in her savings account. She has m dollars in her checking account. Which expression describes how much money she has in both accounts?

   A. $1,293.76 - m$ **B.** $1,293.76 + m$ **C.** $1,293.76m$ **D.** $m - \$1,293.76$

Practice

The ABC Shop sells T-shirts for $12, with no extra cost for putting your name on the T-shirt. Shirts-To-Go sells T-shirts for $10, but they charge $.40 for each letter they put on the T-shirt.

ABC Shop No. of Letters	Cost	Shirts-To-Go No. of Letters	Cost
3		3	
4		4	
5		5	
6		6	
7		7	
8		8	
9		9	
10		10	

1. Complete the table using names of 3 to 10 letters in length.

2. Graph the data for the tables. Label your graph. Where would you go to buy a T-shirt for your own name?

ABC Shop

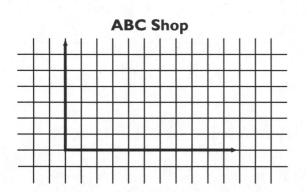

Shirts-To-Go

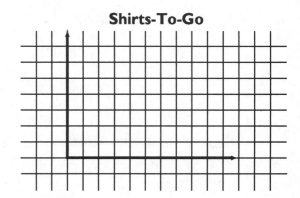

A classroom has four windows that are in a row on one wall. All of the windows can be opened or closed, but the teacher does not like to have two adjacent windows closed.

3. Draw pictures or use symbols to show how many different ways the windows can be opened or closed.

_____

_____

4. Draw pictures or use symbols to show how many different ways the windows can be opened or closed if there are 5 windows in a row.

_____

_____

_____

Practice

State whether the given number is a solution to the equation.

1. $m + 7 = 18; m = 11$

2. $14 = 9 + v; v = 6$

3. $19 = 17 + y; y = 3$

4. $w - 17 = 24; w = 41$

5. $93 = b - 43; b = 146$

6. $53 = m - 14; m = 67$

7. $n - 53 = 69; n = 122$

8. $78 = b + 19; b = 59$

9. $47 + a = 153; a = 104$

Choose algebra tiles, mental math, or a calculator to solve each equation.

10. $t + 19 = 47$

11. $v + 14 = 76$

12. $94 = y + 32$

13. $86 = a + 29$

14. $w - 53 = 76$

15. $53 = z - 19$

16. $112 = x - 74$

17. $49 = c + 19$

18. $b + 24 = 52$

19. $117 = 69 + a$

20. $e - 84 = 79$

21. $62 = g - 27$

If possible, write an equation and solve each problem. If it is not possible to solve, explain why.

22. If two pencils cost $.17, how much will 36 pencils cost?

23. Tomás ran 6 mi. How long will it take him to run 10 mi?

24. A bus can hold 54 people. There are 376 students and teachers going on a field trip. How many buses are needed?

25. It took Bekka 12 min to walk to school. At that rate, how long will it take her to walk to the store?

Practice

State whether the given number is a solution to the equation.

1. $8c = 80$; $c = 10$ **2.** $b \div 7 = 8$; $b = 56$ **3.** $9m = 108$; $m = 12$ **4.** $y \div 9 = 17$; $y = 163$

_____   _____   _____   _____

5. $9r = 72$; $r = 7$ **6.** $14b = 56$; $b = 4$ **7.** $48 = y \div 4$; $y = 12$ **8.** $32 = y \div 8$; $y = 246$

_____   _____   _____   _____

9. $17a = 41$; $a = 3$ **10.** $w \div 21 = 17$; $w = 357$ **11.** $21c = 189$; $c = 8$ **12.** $52 = y \div 6$; $y = 302$

_____   _____   _____   _____

Choose algebra tiles, mental math, or a calculator to solve each equation.

13. $905 = 5a$ **14.** $6v = 792$ **15.** $12 = y \div 12$ **16.** $b \div 18 = 21$

_____   _____   _____   _____

17. $80 = 16b$ **18.** $19m = 266$ **19.** $d \div 1{,}000 = 10$ **20.** $g \div 52 = 18$

_____   _____   _____   _____

21. $672 = 21f$ **22.** $z \div 27 = 63$ **23.** $43h = 817$ **24.** $58 = j \div 71$

_____   _____   _____   _____

25. Lea drove 220 mi and used 12 gal of gas. How many miles per gallon did her car get? _____

26. Ty spent $13.14 on folders that cost $2.19 each. How many folders did he buy?

_____

27. Bob pays a $.40 toll going to and from work. How much does he pay in four weeks, working five days a week?

_____

28. Julia wants to buy copies of a book to give as presents. How many books can she buy if they are on sale for $12 each, and she has $100 to spend? _____

▪▪▪▪Practice

Find the area of each figure. The area of each square is 1 cm².

1.   2.   3.

          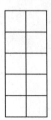

_____   _____   _____

Estimate the area of each figure. Assume that each square represents 1 in.².

4.   5.   6.

_____   _____   _____

7. **Circle A, B, C, or D.** Each square represents 100 m².
   Which is the best estimate for the area of the figure?

   A. 250 m²   **B.** 2,500 m²
   C. 2,000 m²   **D.** 1,500 m²

8. Outline the letters of your first name on the graph paper
   below. Make the letters as large as possible. Shade in the
   letters and then find the area. Each square represents 1
   cm².

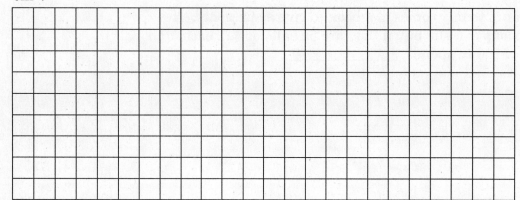

Course 1 • *Chapter 6*

▰▰▰▰Practice

Find the area and perimeter of each rectangle.

1.
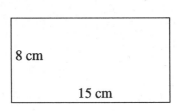

2.
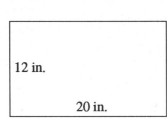

3.
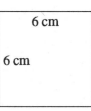

_____   _____   _____

Use a centimeter ruler to measure the length and width of each rectangle. Mark the length and width on each figure. Then find the perimeter and area.

4.

5.
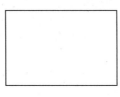

6.

_____   _____   _____

Choose a calculator, paper and pencil, or mental math.

7. The length of a rectangle is 8 cm. The width is 6 cm.

   a. What is the area? _____   **b.** What is the perimeter? _____

8. The area of a rectangle is 45 in.^{2}. One dimension is 5 in. What is the perimeter? _____

9. The perimeter of a square is 24 cm. What is the area of the square? _____

10. The perimeter of a rectangle is 38 cm. The length is 7.5 cm. What is the width? _____

11. The figure at the right contains only squares. Each side of the shaded square is 1 unit. What is the length, width, and area of the figure?

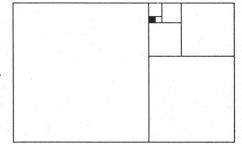

_____

■■■■Practice

Find the area of each figure.

1.

_____

2.

_____

3.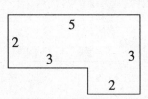

_____

4.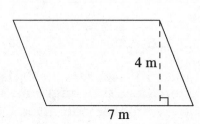

_____

Find the area of each figure by dividing it into polygons.

5.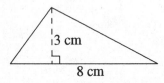

_____

6.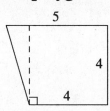

_____

7.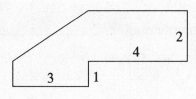

_____

8.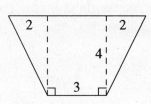

_____

9. Draw and label a triangle and a parallelogram that each have an area of 20 square units.

Tell whether each statement is *true* or *false*.

10. A square is always a rectangle. _____

11. Two triangles that have the same base always have the same area. _____

12. Two rectangles that have the same perimeter always have the same area. _____

Practice

Use 3.14 for π to estimate the circumference of a circle with the given radius, *r*, or diameter, *d*.

1. $d = 4$ in. _____

2. $d = 8$ cm _____

3. $r = 6$ m _____

4. $r = 10$ ft _____

5. $r = 3$ in. _____

6. $d = 20$ cm _____

Use a calculator to find the circumference of a circle with the given radius, *r*, or diameter, *d*. Use 3.14 for π. Round your answer to the nearest tenth.

7. $r = 18$ cm _____

8. $d = 44$ ft _____

9. $r = 28$ in. _____

10. $r = 24$ m _____

11. $d = 36$ in. _____

12. $d = 48$ cm _____

Use a calculator to find the diameter of a circle with the given circumference, *C*. Use 3.14 for π. Round to the nearest unit.

13. $C = 128$ ft _____

14. $C = 36$ cm _____

15. $C = 200$ m _____

16. $C = 85$ in. _____

17. $C = 57$ cm _____

18. $C = 132$ in. _____

Complete the table. Use a metric measuring tape to measure the circumference and the diameter of four different circular objects. Then check to see if the ratio $\frac{C}{d} = \pi$.

Object	Circumference, C	Diameter, d	$\frac{C}{d}$
19.			
20.			
21.			
22.			

23. Use the table you have just completed. What can you conclude about the ratio $\frac{C}{d}$?

_____

Practice

Use a calculator to find the area of a circle with the given radius, *r*, or diameter, *d*. Give each answer to the nearest tenth of a unit.

1. *r* = 12 cm _____

2. *d* = 15 m _____

3. *d* = 9 cm _____

4. *d* = 14 cm _____

5. *r* = 22 m _____

6. *r* = 28 m _____

Use a calculator to find the circumference and area of each circle. Give each answer to the nearest tenth of a unit.

7.

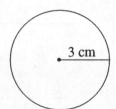

3 cm

_____

8.

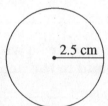

2.5 cm

_____

9.

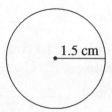

1.5 cm

_____

Use a calculator to find the area of the shaded region. Round to the nearest unit.

10.

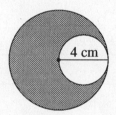

4 cm

_____

11.

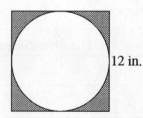

12 in.

_____

Solve each problem. Round to the nearest inch.

12. Find the area of a 8-in. diameter pizza. _____

13. Find the area of a 12-in. diameter pizza. _____

14. The cost of an 8-in. round pizza is $7.00. The cost of a 12-in. round pizza is $12.50.

Which size pizza is the better buy? _____

▰▰▰Practice

Identify each three-dimensional figure.

1.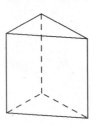

_____

2.

_____

3.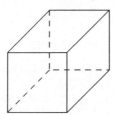

_____

4.

_____

Find the number of faces, edges, and vertices for each figure.

5.

_____

6.

_____

7. **Circle A, B, or C.** Which of the following is *not* a possible view of a rectangular prism?

   A.  **B.**   **C.**

Name the figure you can form from each net.

8.

_____

9.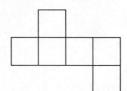

_____

10.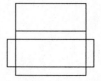

_____

◼️◼️◼️*Practice*

Choose a calculator, paper and pencil, or mental math to find the surface area of the rectangular prism.

1.
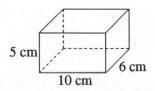
4 in.
4 in.
2 in.

_____

2.
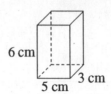
6 cm
5 cm
3 cm

_____

3.
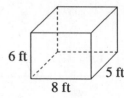
6 ft
8 ft
5 ft

_____

4.
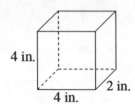
5 cm
10 cm
6 cm

_____

5.
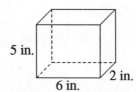
5 in.
6 in.
2 in.

_____

6.
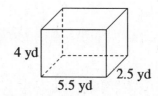
4 yd
5.5 yd
2.5 yd

_____

Find the surface area of the rectangular prism that has the given net.

7.
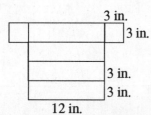
3 in.
3 in.
3 in.
3 in.
12 in.

_____

8.
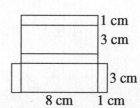
1 cm
3 cm
3 cm
8 cm   1 cm

_____

Draw or build a rectangular tower of centimeter cubes. Make the bottom layer 4 cm by 3 cm, and make 5 layers.

9. How many cubes have at least one side visible? _____

10. How many cubes are hidden from view inside the tower? _____

11. What is the surface area of the tower? _____

▰▰▰▰▰Practice

Find the volume of each rectangular prism.

1.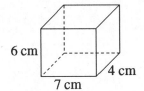

6 cm
4 cm
7 cm

_____

2.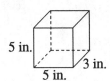

5 in.
3 in.
5 in.

_____

3.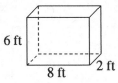

6 ft
2 ft
8 ft

_____

4. $l = 6$ cm, $w = 5$ cm, $h = 12$ cm

_____

5. $l = 13$ in., $w = 7$ in., $h = 9$ in.

_____

The volume and two dimensions of a rectangular prism are given. Find the third dimension.

6. $V = 140$ ft^3, $l = 5$ ft, $h = 7$ ft

_____

7. $V = 255$ cm^3, $w = 17$ cm, $h = 3$ cm

_____

8. $V = 343$ in.^{3}, $h = 7$ in. , $l = 7$ in.

_____

9. $V = 280$ yd^3, $l = 14$ yd, $w = 4$ yd

_____

Draw and label a rectangular prism with the given volume, using a set of whole-number dimensions.

10. $V = 90$ cm^3

11. $V = 125$ cm^3

Solve each problem.

12. A fish aquarium measures 3 ft long, 2 ft wide, and 2 ft high. What is the volume of the aquarium?

_____

13. A swimming pool is 25 ft wide, 60 ft long, and 7 ft deep. What is the volume of the pool? _____

Name _____ Class _____ Date _____

Choose any strategy to solve each problem. Show all your work.

1. Circle the nets that you could fold to form a cube.

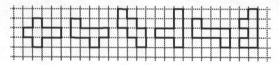

2. Find three numbers that continue the pattern. 1, 3, 7, _____,

   _____, _____

3. Describe two different ways to continue the pattern.

   2, 3, 5, _____, _____, _____

   2, 3, 5, _____, _____, _____

4. How many different rectangles can you form using 24 centimeter blocks?

   _____

5. What is the area of the parallelogram at the right? Assume that each square represents 1 cm².

   _____

6. **Circle A, B, or C.** Which piece of plastic wrap shown below can be used to cover the surface of the box shown? The piece can overlap, but cannot be cut.

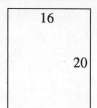

A. 12 / 16   **B.** 16 / 20   **C.** 12 / 12

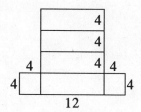

7. A farmer has 3 sons. The farmer decides to give each son the same amount of seeds and barrels. The farmer has 21 barrels: 7 are full of seeds, 7 are half-full, 7 are empty. You cannot move seeds from one barrel to another. How can the farmer divide the seed and barrels equally? Make a model to help solve.

   _____

   _____

© Prentice-Hall, Inc.

▰▰▰ *Practice*

Use mental math to determine whether the first number is divisible by the second.

1. 475; 5 _____

2. 5,296; 3 _____

3. 843; 2 _____

4. 76,780; 10 _____

5. 456,790; 5 _____

6. 3,460; 2 _____

7. 4,197; 3 _____

8. 100,005; 10 _____

Use mental math to determine whether each number is divisible by 1, 2, 3, 5, 9, or 10.

9. 126

10. 257

11. 430

12. 535

_____

_____

_____

_____

13. 745

14. 896

15. 729

16. 945

_____

_____

_____

_____

17. 4,580

18. 6,331

19. 7,952

20. 8,000

_____

_____

_____

_____

21. 19,450

22. 21,789

23. 43,785

24. 28,751

_____

_____

_____

_____

Find the digit to make each number divisible by 9.

25. 54,78☐

26. 42,☐97

27. 83,2☐4

28. 53☐,904

Circle A, B, C, or D. Which number satisfies the given conditions?

29. divisible by 1, 3, and 5

A. 10

B. 93

C. 45

D. 54

30. divisible by 1, 2, 3, and 9

A. 18

B. 9

C. 6

D. 60

31. divisible by 1, 2, 5, and 10

A. 406

B. 400

C. 205

D. 716

32. divisible by 1, 2, 3, 5, and 10

A. 708

B. 65

C. 200

D. 600

33. There are 159 students to be grouped into relay teams. Each team is to have the same number of students. Can each team have 3, 5, or 6 students?

_____

Practice

1. The diagram below shows the different rectangles that can be formed using exactly 24 square tiles. Use the diagram to determine all the factors of 24.

_____

  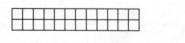

Tell whether each number is prime or composite.

2. 53

3. 86

4. 95

5. 17

_____ _____ _____ _____

6. 24

7. 27

8. 31

9. 51

_____ _____ _____ _____

10. 103

11. 47

12. 93

13. 56

_____ _____ _____ _____

Complete each factor tree.

14.

15.

16.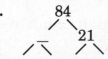

17.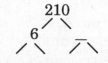

Find the prime factorization of each number using a factor tree.

18. 58

19. 72

20. 40

21. 30

_____ _____ _____ _____

22. 120

23. 100

24. 144

25. 310

_____ _____ _____ _____

Find the number with the given prime factorization.

26. $2 \times 2 \times 5 \times 7 \times 11$

27. $2 \times 3 \times 5 \times 7 \times 11$

_____ _____

28. $2 \times 2 \times 13 \times 17$

29. $7 \times 11 \times 13 \times 17$

_____ _____

■Practice

Make a list to find the GCF of each set of numbers.

1. 8, 12 _____

2. 18, 27 _____

3. 15, 23 _____

4. 17, 34 _____

5. 24, 12 _____

6. 18, 24 _____

7. 5, 25 _____

8. 20, 25 _____

9. 10, 15 _____

10. 25, 75 _____

11. 14, 21 _____

12. 18, 57 _____

13. 32, 24, 40 _____

14. 25, 60, 75 _____

15. 12, 35, 15 _____

16. 15, 35, 20 _____

Use prime factorization to find the GCF of each set of numbers.

17. 28, 24 _____

18. 27, 36 _____

19. 15, 305 _____

20. 24, 45 _____

21. 57, 27 _____

22. 24, 48 _____

23. 56, 35 _____

24. 29, 87 _____

25. 75, 200 _____

26. 90, 160 _____

27. 72, 108 _____

28. 50, 96 _____

29. 8, 42, 60 _____

30. 75, 90, 120 _____

31. 45, 70, 120 _____

32. 200, 450, 300 _____

33. The GCF of two numbers is 850. One number is *not* a multiple of the other. What are the smallest two numbers these two could be?

_____

34. The GCF of two numbers is 479. One number is even, and the other number is odd. One number is *not* a multiple of the other. What are the smallest two numbers these two could be?

_____

35. The GCF of two numbers is 871. Both of the numbers are even, and neither is a multiple of the other. What are the smallest two numbers these could be?

_____

Practice

Name the fraction modeled by each fraction bar.

1.

_____

2.

_____

3.

_____

4.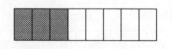

_____

5.

_____

6.

_____

7.

_____

8.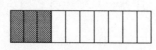

_____

9.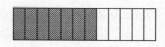

_____

10.

_____

11.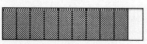

_____

12.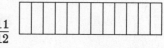

_____

Model each fraction using the given fraction bar.

13. $\frac{1}{12}$

14. $\frac{5}{12}$

15. $\frac{11}{12}$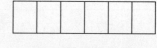

16. $\frac{2}{6}$

17. $\frac{4}{6}$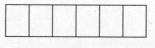

18. $\frac{1}{6}$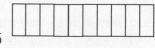

19. $\frac{7}{10}$

20. $\frac{9}{10}$

21. $\frac{5}{10}$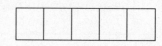

22. $\frac{3}{5}$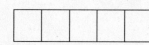

23. $\frac{2}{5}$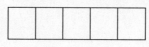

24. $\frac{4}{5}$

Circle A, B, C, or D.

25. Which fraction is closest to 0?

   A. $\frac{3}{4}$ **B.** $\frac{7}{8}$ **C.** $\frac{11}{15}$ **D.** $\frac{1}{12}$

26. Which fraction is closest to $\frac{1}{2}$?

   A. $\frac{11}{25}$ **B.** $\frac{1}{16}$ **C.** $\frac{9}{10}$ **D.** $\frac{1}{40}$

Practice

Name the fractions modeled. Tell whether they are equivalent.

1.

2.

3.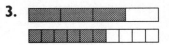

_____   _____   _____

Complete each equation with the appropriate fraction.

4. $\frac{3}{4} \times \boxed{} = \frac{9}{12}$

5. $\frac{70}{80} \div \boxed{} = \frac{7}{8}$

6. $\frac{15}{60} \div \boxed{} = \frac{1}{4}$

7. $\frac{3}{8} \times \boxed{} = \frac{15}{40}$

8. $\frac{75}{100} \div \boxed{} = \frac{3}{4}$

9. $\frac{7}{10} \times \boxed{} = \frac{42}{60}$

Write two fractions equivalent to each fraction.

10. $\frac{3}{10}$ _____

11. $\frac{7}{8}$ _____

12. $\frac{5}{6}$ _____

13. $\frac{3}{4}$ _____

14. $\frac{15}{20}$ _____

15. $\frac{8}{12}$ _____

16. $\frac{15}{45}$ _____

17. $\frac{8}{32}$ _____

State whether each fraction is in simplest form. If not, write it in simplest form.

18. $\frac{15}{35}$ _____

19. $\frac{22}{55}$ _____

20. $\frac{11}{15}$ _____

21. $\frac{25}{32}$ _____

22. $\frac{34}{36}$ _____

23. $\frac{19}{57}$ _____

24. $\frac{20}{53}$ _____

25. $\frac{125}{200}$ _____

26. $\frac{27}{54}$ _____

27. $\frac{30}{41}$ _____

28. $\frac{9}{17}$ _____

29. $\frac{85}{110}$ _____

30. Use the numbers 2, 5, 8, and 20 to write two pairs of equivalent fractions.

_____

■■■■■*Practice*

Choose a calculator, paper and pencil, or mental math to simplify each fraction.

1. $\frac{8}{12}$ _____

2. $\frac{15}{60}$ _____

3. $\frac{54}{108}$ _____

4. $\frac{132}{144}$ _____

5. $\frac{17}{51}$ _____

6. $\frac{26}{78}$ _____

7. $\frac{27}{45}$ _____

8. $\frac{42}{45}$ _____

9. $\frac{87}{96}$ _____

10. $\frac{156}{176}$ _____

11. $\frac{65}{135}$ _____

12. $\frac{81}{153}$ _____

13. $\frac{96}{180}$ _____

14. $\frac{132}{187}$ _____

15. $\frac{195}{615}$ _____

16. $\frac{324}{513}$ _____

Write each fraction in simplest form.

17. $\frac{56}{64}$ _____

18. $\frac{45}{75}$ _____

19. $\frac{24}{32}$ _____

20. $\frac{10}{15}$ _____

21. $\frac{56}{70}$ _____

22. $\frac{48}{64}$ _____

23. $\frac{54}{135}$ _____

24. $\frac{144}{252}$ _____

25. $\frac{42}{112}$ _____

26. $\frac{100}{125}$ _____

27. $\frac{160}{176}$ _____

28. $\frac{120}{216}$ _____

29. $\frac{85}{136}$ _____

30. $\frac{216}{408}$ _____

31. $\frac{192}{368}$ _____

32. $\frac{180}{765}$ _____

Circle A, B, C, or D. Which fraction is *not* equivalent to the given fraction?

33. $\frac{3}{4}$

A. $\frac{12}{16}$ B. $\frac{9}{13}$

C. $\frac{15}{20}$ D. $\frac{18}{24}$

34. $\frac{4}{5}$

A. $\frac{40}{50}$ B. $\frac{44}{55}$

C. $\frac{35}{45}$ D. $\frac{48}{60}$

Practice

Circle A, B, C, or D. Find the mixed number that represents the amount shaded in each model.

1.

    A. $2\frac{1}{4}$ **B.** $1\frac{3}{4}$ **C.** $2\frac{3}{4}$ **D.** $3\frac{3}{4}$

2.

    A. $4\frac{5}{6}$ **B.** $3\frac{5}{6}$ **C.** $2\frac{5}{6}$ **D.** $3\frac{1}{6}$

3.

    A. $4\frac{5}{8}$ **B.** $4\frac{3}{8}$ **C.** $5\frac{5}{8}$ **D.** $5\frac{3}{8}$

4.

    A. $5\frac{3}{5}$ **B.** $4\frac{2}{5}$ **C.** $6\frac{2}{5}$ **D.** $5\frac{2}{5}$

Write each improper fraction as a mixed number.

5. $\frac{15}{2}$ _____   6. $\frac{8}{3}$ _____   7. $\frac{5}{2}$ _____   8. $\frac{7}{3}$ _____

9. $\frac{11}{10}$ _____   10. $\frac{7}{6}$ _____   11. $\frac{9}{8}$ _____   12. $\frac{11}{8}$ _____

13. $\frac{15}{8}$ _____   14. $\frac{21}{4}$ _____   15. $\frac{17}{3}$ _____   16. $\frac{17}{4}$ _____

17. $\frac{17}{5}$ _____   18. $\frac{17}{6}$ _____   19. $\frac{21}{10}$ _____   20. $\frac{25}{4}$ _____

Write each mixed number as an improper fraction.

21. $1\frac{7}{8}$ _____   22. $2\frac{3}{4}$ _____   23. $7\frac{1}{3}$ _____   24. $8\frac{1}{2}$ _____

25. $3\frac{3}{4}$ _____   26. $4\frac{4}{7}$ _____   27. $5\frac{5}{6}$ _____   28. $1\frac{9}{10}$ _____

29. $2\frac{3}{8}$ _____   30. $4\frac{7}{8}$ _____   31. $2\frac{3}{5}$ _____   32. $6\frac{7}{8}$ _____

33. $3\frac{11}{12}$ _____   34. $2\frac{7}{12}$ _____   35. $5\frac{4}{15}$ _____   36. $2\frac{7}{15}$ _____

▰▰▰ Practice

Find the LCM of each set of numbers. Use lists of multiples of each number.

1. 5, 10

_____

2. 2, 3

_____

3. 6, 8

_____

4. 4, 6

_____

5. 8, 10

_____

6. 5, 6

_____

7. 12, 15

_____

8. 8, 12

_____

9. 9, 15

_____

10. 6, 15

_____

11. 6, 9

_____

12. 6, 18

_____

13. 3, 5

_____

14. 4, 5

_____

15. 9, 21

_____

16. 7, 28

_____

17. 4, 6, 8

_____

18. 6, 8, 12

_____

19. 4, 9, 12

_____

20. 6, 9, 12

_____

21. 6, 12, 15

_____

22. 8, 12, 15

_____

Find the LCM of each set of numbers. Use prime factorization.

23. 18, 21

_____

24. 15, 21

_____

25. 18, 24

_____

26. 21, 24

_____

27. 15, 30

_____

28. 24, 30

_____

29. 24, 72

_____

30. 18, 72

_____

31. 8, 42

_____

32. 16, 42

_____

33. 8, 56

_____

34. 6, 81

_____

35. 8, 30

_____

36. 16, 30

_____

37. 18, 30

_____

38. 45, 60

_____

39. 12, 24, 16

_____

40. 8, 16, 20

_____

41. 12, 16, 20

_____

42. 15, 20, 25

_____

43. At one store hot dogs come in packages of eight. Hot dog buns come in packages of twelve. What is the least number of packages of each type that you can buy and have no hot dogs or buns left over?

_____

Practice

Compare using <, =, or >.

1. $2\frac{14}{17}$ ☐ $1\frac{16}{17}$ **2.** $\frac{15}{21}$ ☐ $\frac{5}{7}$ **3.** $2\frac{7}{8}$ ☐ $2\frac{5}{6}$ **4.** $1\frac{1}{2}$ ☐ $2\frac{1}{3}$

5. $3\frac{15}{16}$ ☐ $3\frac{21}{32}$ **6.** $4\frac{7}{8}$ ☐ $3\frac{9}{10}$ **7.** $5\frac{9}{10}$ ☐ $5\frac{18}{20}$ **8.** $4\frac{7}{8}$ ☐ $5\frac{1}{8}$

9. $1\frac{19}{20}$ ☐ $2\frac{1}{20}$ **10.** $4\frac{5}{6}$ ☐ $5\frac{19}{20}$ **11.** $7\frac{3}{10}$ ☐ $7\frac{9}{30}$ **12.** $2\frac{7}{15}$ ☐ $1\frac{14}{15}$

13. $4\frac{19}{24}$ ☐ $4\frac{7}{12}$ **14.** $5\frac{19}{20}$ ☐ $6\frac{21}{22}$ **15.** $4\frac{15}{20}$ ☐ $4\frac{21}{28}$ **16.** $\frac{27}{30}$ ☐ $1\frac{1}{4}$

Order each set of numbers from least to greatest.

17. $\frac{9}{10}, \frac{5}{6}, \frac{14}{15}$

18. $1\frac{7}{8}, 1\frac{7}{12}, 1\frac{5}{6}$

19. $\frac{14}{15}, \frac{9}{10}, \frac{11}{12}$

_____   _____   _____

20. $2\frac{1}{4}, 4\frac{1}{6}, 3\frac{7}{8}, 3\frac{5}{6}$

21. $\frac{2}{3}, 1\frac{4}{5}, 1\frac{7}{30}, 1\frac{11}{15}$

22. $2\frac{1}{6}, 1\frac{3}{4}, 3\frac{7}{8}, 2\frac{1}{10}$

_____   _____   _____

23. $\frac{5}{12}, \frac{17}{30}, \frac{19}{25}, \frac{3}{5}$

24. $1\frac{5}{6}, 2\frac{1}{6}, 1\frac{11}{12}, 1\frac{11}{18}$

25. $3\frac{7}{15}, \frac{17}{20}, 1\frac{18}{25}, 2\frac{31}{36}$

_____   _____   _____

Circle A, B, C, or D.

26. Which fraction is greater than $\frac{31}{36}$?

   A. $\frac{2}{3}$ **B.** $\frac{5}{8}$

   C. $\frac{1}{2}$ **D.** $\frac{13}{24}$

27. Which fraction is less than $\frac{8}{15}$?

   A. $\frac{4}{7}$ **B.** $\frac{3}{5}$

   C. $\frac{17}{30}$ **D.** $\frac{4}{9}$

Practice

Write the decimal number represented by each model.
Write this decimal as a fraction in simplest form.

1.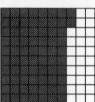

2.

3.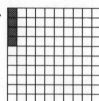

_____   _____   _____

Write each decimal as a fraction in simplest form.

4. 0.6 _____   **5.** 0.25 _____   **6.** 0.74 _____   **7.** 0.29 _____

8. 0.635 _____   **9.** 0.8 _____   **10.** 0.14 _____   **11.** 0.95 _____

12. 0.645 _____   **13.** 0.782 _____   **14.** 0.493 _____   **15.** 0.758 _____

Write each fraction as a decimal. Use a bar to show repeating decimals.

16. $\frac{5}{6}$ _____   **17.** $\frac{7}{8}$ _____   **18.** $\frac{9}{16}$ _____   **19.** $\frac{4}{25}$ _____

20. $\frac{1}{12}$ _____   **21.** $\frac{4}{15}$ _____   **22.** $\frac{9}{100}$ _____   **23.** $\frac{8}{9}$ _____

24. $\frac{7}{25}$ _____   **25.** $\frac{3}{50}$ _____   **26.** $\frac{1}{125}$ _____   **27.** $\frac{6}{11}$ _____

Circle A, B, C, or D. Which set of numbers is in order from least to greatest?

28. $\frac{1}{2}$, 0.75, $\frac{5}{8}$, 0.9, $\frac{7}{10}$

   A. $\frac{1}{2}$, $\frac{5}{8}$, 0.75, $\frac{7}{10}$, 0.9   **B.** $\frac{1}{2}$, $\frac{5}{8}$, $\frac{7}{10}$, 0.75, 0.9

   C. 0.9, 0.75, $\frac{7}{10}$, $\frac{5}{8}$, $\frac{1}{2}$ **D.** $\frac{1}{2}$, 0.75, $\frac{5}{8}$, $\frac{7}{10}$, 0.9

29. 0.875, $\frac{9}{10}$, $\frac{15}{16}$, 0.98

   A. 0.98, $\frac{15}{16}$, $\frac{9}{10}$, 0.875   **B.** $\frac{15}{16}$, $\frac{9}{10}$, 0.875, 0.98

   C. $\frac{9}{10}$, 0.875, $\frac{15}{16}$, 0.98   **D.** 0.875, $\frac{9}{10}$, $\frac{15}{16}$, 0.98

Practice

Work backward to solve.

1. At the end of a board game, Theo had $57. During the game he had won $200, lost $150, won $25, lost $10, and lost $35. How much money did Theo have when the game started?

   _____

2. Jan spent half of the money she had on a new winter coat. Later, she spent half of what remained on a new dress. Next, she spent half of what remained on a pair of boots. She returned home with $57. How much money did Jan have before she started shopping ?

   _____

3. Bill gathered some eggs on Monday. On Tuesday, he gathered half as many eggs, plus an egg, as what he gathered on Monday. On Wednesday, he gathered half the difference of the number of eggs he gathered on Monday and Tuesday, plus an egg. If he gathered 5 eggs on Wednesday, how many eggs did Bill gather on Monday?

   _____

4. Carli spent a third of her money, and then spent $4 more. She then spent half of what money remained. It cost her $1 for the bus ride home. She then had $5 left. How much money did she start with?

   _____

5. Mick picked a number, doubled it, added 8, divided by 4, and had a result of 12. What number did Mick pick?

   _____

6. It takes Jenni 50 minutes to get ready for school. The drive to school takes 15 minutes. She needs 8 minutes to get to her locker, then to her first class. If school begins at 8:30 A.M., what is the latest Jenni should get up in the morning?

   _____

7. On May 31, Hayden's uncle and grandfather came to visit him. Hayden's grandfather visits every three days, and his uncle visits every twelve days. What is the first day in May that both visited Hayden on the same day?

   _____

**Practice**

Round each measurement to the nearest half inch.

1. $2\frac{4}{5}$ _____   2. $3\frac{1}{8}$ _____   3. $\frac{17}{16}$ _____   4. $4\frac{1}{2}$ _____

Round each measurement to the nearest inch.

5. $1\frac{3}{8}$ _____   6. $5\frac{3}{4}$ _____   7. $6\frac{5}{16}$ _____   8. $9\frac{5}{8}$ _____

Write the fraction modeled by each fraction bar. Then round to the nearest $\frac{1}{2}$.

9.

_____

10.

_____

Estimate each sum or difference.

11. $\frac{3}{4} + \frac{3}{8}$

_____

12. $\frac{7}{10} - \frac{1}{6}$

_____

13. $5\frac{7}{8} + 3\frac{3}{4}$

_____

14. $8\frac{1}{12} - 3\frac{9}{10}$

_____

15. $6\frac{5}{7} - 2\frac{2}{9}$

_____

16. $3\frac{5}{8} + 2\frac{3}{10}$

_____

17. Name three fractions that round to $\frac{1}{2}$.

_____

18. Name three fractions that round to 1.

_____

19. The fabric for the play costumes costs $5.95/yd. Patti needs $2\frac{7}{8}$ yd for one costume and $3\frac{5}{8}$ yd for another one. About how much will she spend on these costumes?

_____

20. One bag of oranges costs $2.99 and weighs about $3\frac{7}{8}$ lb. Individual oranges are sold at $.89/lb. Which is the better buy? Explain.

_____

_____

_____

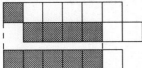**Practice**

Write an addition sentence for each model.

1.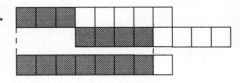

_____

2.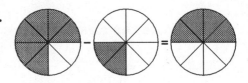

_____

Write a subtraction sentence for each model.

3.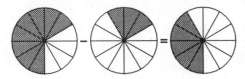

_____

4.

_____

Draw a model and find each sum or difference.

5. $\frac{1}{4} + \frac{2}{4} =$ _____

6. $\frac{7}{10} - \frac{4}{10} =$ _____

7. $\frac{5}{8} - \frac{3}{8} =$ _____

8. $\frac{1}{8} + \frac{5}{8} =$ _____

Use mental math to decide if the answer will be greater than 1. Write yes or no. Then add or subtract.

9. $\frac{5}{8} + \frac{2}{8}$ _____

10. $\frac{3}{10} + \frac{9}{10}$ _____

11. $\frac{11}{12} - \frac{5}{12}$ _____

12. $\frac{11}{16} - \frac{3}{16}$ _____

13. $\frac{3}{6} + \frac{4}{6}$ _____

14. $\frac{7}{9} - \frac{3}{9}$ _____

15. What is the total amount of sugar the recipe at the right calls for?

_____

16. Martha decides to double the recipe. How much brown sugar will she use?

_____

Martha's Cookie Recipe
1 cup shortening
2 eggs
$\frac{3}{4}$ cup white sugar
$\frac{3}{4}$ cup brown sugar
$1\frac{1}{2}$ cup flour
1 teaspoon vanilla

Name _____ Class _____ Date _____

Write a number sentence for each model.

1.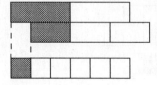

   _____

2.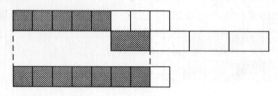

   _____

Write the LCD. Then add or subtract.

3. $\frac{1}{4} + \frac{2}{3}$ _____

4. $\frac{2}{5} - \frac{1}{10}$ _____

5. $\frac{1}{6} + \frac{1}{4}$ _____

Add or subtract. Write the answer in simplest form.

6. $\frac{5}{8} + \frac{1}{4}$ _____

7. $\frac{7}{8} - \frac{1}{2}$ _____

8. $\frac{3}{10} + \frac{4}{5}$ _____

9. $\frac{5}{6} - \frac{2}{5}$ _____

10. $\frac{5}{12} - \frac{1}{4}$ _____

11. $\frac{7}{16} + \frac{1}{8}$ _____

12. $\frac{1}{4} + \frac{7}{16} + \frac{5}{8}$ _____

13. $\frac{2}{3} + \frac{1}{2} + \frac{11}{12}$ _____

Use estimation to decide if the answer is greater or less than 1. Write > or <. Then add or subtract.

14. $\frac{2}{7} + \frac{1}{2}$ _____

15. $\frac{4}{5} - \frac{3}{4}$ _____

16. $\frac{2}{3} - \frac{1}{6}$ _____

17. $\frac{5}{8} + \frac{2}{3}$ _____

18. $\frac{5}{7} - \frac{1}{5}$ _____

19. $\frac{3}{5} + \frac{7}{10}$ _____

Find x. Write the answer in simplest form.

20. $x = \frac{1}{3} + \frac{5}{6}$ _____

21. $\frac{4}{5} - \frac{1}{3} = x$ _____

22. $\frac{11}{12} - \frac{2}{5} = x$ _____

23. $x = \frac{5}{8} + \frac{11}{12}$ _____

24. Jeanie has a $\frac{3}{4}$-yd piece of ribbon. She needs one $\frac{3}{8}$-yd piece and one $\frac{1}{2}$-yd piece . Can she cut the piece of ribbon into the two smaller pieces? Explain. Draw a model that shows the problem.

_____

_____

© Prentice-Hall, Inc.

Practice

Juanita is building a maze for the school carnival. She uses red cord to mark the path from the beginning of the maze to the end. She uses a table and a spreadsheet to find how much cord she will need.

Complete the table for Juanita.

Distance (parts of a km)	Sum
$\frac{1}{256}$	$\frac{1}{256}$
$\frac{1}{256} + \frac{1}{128}$	$\frac{3}{256}$

1. _____

2. _____

3. _____

4. _____

5. _____

6. _____

7. _____

Juanita needs to order the rope using a decimal value.
Complete the spreadsheet for Juanita.

		A	B	C	D
	1	Segment	Numerator of the Sum	Denominator of the Sum	Sum as a Decimal
	2	1	1	256	0.004
	3	2	3	256	0.012
8.	4	3			
9.	5	4			
10.	6	5			
11.	7	6			
12.	8	7			
13.	9	8			
14.	10	9			

Practice

Complete to rename each mixed number.

1. $4\frac{3}{8} = 3\frac{\blacksquare}{8}$ _____

2. $6\frac{1}{4} = 5\frac{\blacksquare}{4}$ _____

3. $3\frac{5}{12} = 2\frac{\blacksquare}{12}$ _____

Add or subtract.

4. $4\frac{3}{10} + 5\frac{2}{5}$ _____

5. $3\frac{7}{8} + 2\frac{1}{2}$ _____

6. $5\frac{2}{3} + 3\frac{1}{4}$ _____

7. $10\frac{11}{16} - 3\frac{7}{8}$ _____

8. $8\frac{1}{3} - 2\frac{3}{8}$ _____

9. $9 - 3\frac{2}{5}$ _____

10. $7\frac{1}{3} + 5\frac{11}{12}$ _____

11. $11\frac{7}{10} - 4$ _____

12. $2\frac{2}{3} + 4\frac{3}{4}$ _____

13. $5\frac{3}{16} - 2\frac{3}{8}$ _____

14. $8\frac{1}{6} - 3\frac{2}{5}$ _____

15. $7\frac{1}{2} + 3\frac{3}{5}$ _____

16. **Circle A, B, C, or D.** Which two mixed numbers are equivalent to $4\frac{2}{5}$?

A. $4\frac{1}{10}$ and $3\frac{7}{10}$

B. $4\frac{7}{5}$ and $3\frac{5}{2}$

C. $4\frac{4}{10}$ and $3\frac{7}{5}$

D. $4\frac{4}{10}$ and $3\frac{7}{10}$

17. Estimate the length of rope needed to go around a triangle with sides $6\frac{1}{2}$ ft, $7\frac{3}{4}$ ft, and $10\frac{1}{4}$ ft. _____

18. Robbie needs to buy fencing for his square vegetable garden that measures $16\frac{3}{4}$ ft on a side. One side borders the back of the garage. The fencing costs \$4/ft. Estimate how much the fencing for the vegetable garden will cost. _____

19. Paula has 2 yd of elastic. One project needs a piece $\frac{3}{4}$ yd. Does she have enough for another project that needs $1\frac{1}{3}$ yd? Explain.

_____

_____

20. Use a ruler or measuring tape to find the perimeter of your desk. Measure to the nearest half inch.

width:_____   length:_____   perimeter:_____

▄▄▄▄*Practice*

Frank is laying ceramic tiles on a rectangular floor. He wants the perimeter tiles to be a different color for two rows around the edges of the room. The dimensions of the room are 20 ft by 10 ft. Each tile is a square that measures 1 ft on a side.

1. Use two colors to show the two colors of tiles that Frank will install on the floor.

2. How many border tiles does he need? _____

3. How many inside tiles does he need? _____

Draw a diagram to solve.

4. Jessica is hanging five posters on a 19-ft wall. Each poster is 2 ft wide, and she wants to have 1 ft of space between the posters and an equal amount of space at both ends. Draw a diagram to show the placement of the posters.

5. Suppose you are hanging posters along a 35-ft wall in the hallway. Each poster is 2 ft wide.

a. What is the greatest number of posters that you could fit along the wall? _____

b. What is the greatest number of posters that you could fit along the wall if you kept 2 ft between them? Draw a diagram below to show your answer.

Choose any strategy to solve.

6. Matthew earns $.10 for each local newspaper he delivers twice a week. His brother earns $.25 for delivering each Sunday newspaper. They deliver papers to the same number of houses and together they earn $13.95/wk. How many papers does each boy deliver each week?

_____

7. Megan's car averaged 336 mi on 12 gal of gas. How many gallons of gas did Megan use to drive 1,344 mi on vacation?

_____

Practice

Draw a model to represent each product.

1. $\frac{1}{6}$ of $\frac{3}{4}$

2. $\frac{2}{5}$ of $\frac{1}{2}$

Estimate each product.

3. $2\frac{5}{6} \times 1\frac{3}{4}$ _____

4. $3\frac{3}{8} \times 7\frac{1}{4}$ _____

5. $5\frac{3}{8} \times 2\frac{7}{8}$ _____

6. $\frac{7}{8} \times 10$ _____

7. $12 \times \frac{1}{8}$ _____

8. $6 \times \frac{2}{3}$ _____

Find each product.

9. $\frac{4}{5} \times \frac{5}{8}$ _____

10. $\frac{5}{6} \times \frac{3}{8}$ _____

11. $\frac{3}{5} \times \frac{1}{2}$ _____

12. $5 \times 4\frac{1}{3}$ _____

13. $\frac{3}{4} \times 12$ _____

14. $15 \times \frac{2}{5}$ _____

15. $14\frac{1}{6} \times 3\frac{2}{5}$ _____

16. $3\frac{3}{4} \times 5\frac{1}{3}$ _____

17. $2\frac{7}{10} \times 2\frac{2}{3}$ _____

18. $8 \times \frac{3}{16}$ _____

19. $\frac{1}{4} \times 5\frac{2}{5}$ _____

20. $2\frac{3}{8} \times \frac{4}{5}$ _____

21. **Circle A, B, C, or D.** Which product does the model represent?

    A. $\frac{1}{4} \times \frac{2}{3}$

    B. $\frac{3}{4} \times \frac{1}{12}$

    C. $\frac{2}{3} \times \frac{1}{2}$

    D. $\frac{1}{4} \times \frac{1}{2}$

22. Ken used a piece of lumber to build a bookshelf. If he made three shelves that are each $2\frac{1}{2}$ ft long , how long was the piece of lumber? _____

23. Deanna's cake recipe needs to be doubled for a party. How much of each ingredient should Deanna use?

Delicious Cake		
flour	$2\frac{1}{4}$ c	_____
sugar	$1\frac{3}{4}$ c	_____
butter	$1\frac{1}{2}$ c	_____
milk	$\frac{3}{4}$ c	_____

Practice

Write the reciprocal of each number.

1. $\frac{7}{10}$ _____   **2.** 4 _____   **3.** $5\frac{1}{3}$ _____   **4.** $\frac{1}{12}$ _____

5. Draw a diagram to show how many $\frac{3}{4}$-ft pieces of string can be cut from a piece of string $4\frac{1}{2}$ ft long.

Divide. Write each answer in simplest form.

6. $\frac{3}{10} \div \frac{4}{5}$ _____   **7.** $\frac{3}{8} \div 3$ _____   **8.** $3 \div 1\frac{4}{5}$ _____

9. $2\frac{1}{5} \div 1\frac{5}{6}$ _____   **10.** $1\frac{1}{2} \div \frac{3}{16}$ _____   **11.** $\frac{1}{4} \div \frac{1}{8}$ _____

12. $1\frac{7}{8} \div \frac{5}{8}$ _____   **13.** $1\frac{3}{4} \div \frac{1}{16}$ _____   **14.** $3 \div \frac{3}{8}$ _____

15. How many $\frac{3}{4}$-c servings are there in a 6-c package of rice?

_____

16. George divided 5 oranges into quarters. How many pieces of orange did he have? _____

Anna bought a package of ribbon 10 yd long. She needs $1\frac{1}{3}$-yd pieces for a bulletin board.

17. How many pieces can Anna cut from the ribbon?

_____

18. Anna decides to use $\frac{2}{3}$-yd pieces. How many pieces can she cut? _____

19. A bulletin board is 56 in. wide and 36 in. high. How many $3\frac{1}{2}$-in. columns can be created?

_____

20. Study the tangram pieces at the right. If the entire square is 1, find the fractional value of each piece. You can cut the tangram pieces to compare them.

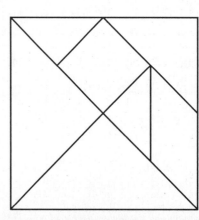

Practice

Complete.

1. $7\frac{1}{2}$ ft = _____ yd

2. 45 in. = _____ ft

3. $1\frac{1}{4}$ mi = _____ ft

4. $2\frac{1}{2}$ lb = _____ oz

5. 28 fl oz = _____ c

6. $2\frac{3}{4}$ T = _____ lb

7. 3 lb = _____ oz

8. 10 pt = _____ qt

Write <, >, or =.

9. $4\frac{1}{3}$ ft ☐ 50 in.

10. 136 oz ☐ $8\frac{1}{2}$ lb

11. 26 fl oz ☐ 3 c

12. 5 qt ☐ $1\frac{1}{4}$ gal

13. 8 yd ☐ 21 ft

14. 4,500 lb ☐ $3\frac{1}{2}$ t

15. The odometer of an automobile shows tenths of a mile. How many feet are in $\frac{1}{10}$ mi? _____

16. How many inches are in one mile? _____

17. Jody bought 3 containers of cottage cheese, each weighing 24 oz. How many pounds did she buy? _____

18. Katie poured 12 oz of juice from a full 6-qt container. How many cups were left in the container? _____

19. The food committee for the end-of-the-year class picnic plans to serve 4-oz hamburger patties. How many pounds of meat should be bought to make 125 hamburgers? _____

Add or subtract. Rename when necessary.

20. 8 ft 3 in.
    $-$3 ft 5 in.

21. 12 qt 1 pt
    $+$11 qt 1 pt

22. 9 yd 15 in.
    $+$7 yd 28 in.

23. 105 lb 8 oz
    $-$98 lb 12 oz

24. 3 c 7 fl oz
    $+$4 c 6 fl oz

25. 13 yd 2 ft
    $-$6 yd 1 ft

© Prentice-Hall, Inc.

Practice

Write each ratio in three ways.

1. saws to pliers

_____

2. hammers to nails

_____

3. saws to nails

_____

4. nails to saws

_____

5. hammers to pliers

_____

6. pliers to saws

_____

7. pliers to nails

_____

8. saws to hammers

_____

9. nails to hammers

_____

**Write a ratio in simplest form to compare the areas of
the figures shown at the right.**

10. triangle to square   _____

11. triangle to parallelogram   _____

12. square to parallelogram   _____

13. square to triangle   _____

14. In Tanya's family, 6 out of 15 people have blue eyes. What
    is the ratio of those who have blue eyes to those who do
    not? _____

15. In Fred's class, 8 of the 21 students earned a grade of B or
    better. What is the ratio of students who did not earn at
    least a B to those who did? _____

16. In Todd's class, 14 of the students own cats and 9 of the
    students own dogs. What is the ratio of dog owners to cat
    owners? _____

17. In Markita's class, there are 15 boys and 12 girls. Write
    two ratios that represent the number of girls to the
    number of boys.

    _____

Practice

Write three equal ratios for each given ratio.

1. 8 : 24   **2.** 15 to 25   **3.** 18 : 36   **4.** $\frac{12}{15}$

_____   _____   _____   _____

_____   _____   _____   _____

Find the value that makes the ratios equal.

5. $\frac{7}{8} = \frac{\blacksquare}{32}$ **6.** $\frac{5}{4} = \frac{15}{\blacksquare}$ **7.** 8 to 12 = $\blacksquare$ to 6   **8.** 9 : 12 = 3 : $\blacksquare$

_____   _____   _____   _____

Write each ratio as a fraction in simplest form.

9. pencils : squares **10.** flowers : pencils **11.** pencils : flowers **12.** pencils : circles

_____   _____   _____   _____

13. squares : flowers **14.** flowers : squares **15.** squares : pencils **16.** circles : flowers

_____   _____   _____   _____

Find the unit rate for each situation.

17. 20 mi in 2 h   **18.** 20 dogs in 10 kennels   **19.** 450 mi in 5 da

_____   _____   _____

20. $60 for 5 books   **21.** 315 grapes for 15 children   **22.** 20 dimes for 4 children

_____   _____   _____

Circle A, B, or C. For each exercise, choose the expression that represents the greatest number.

23. A. $\frac{9}{27}$ B. $\frac{8}{12}$ C. $\frac{2}{2}$ **24.** A. $\frac{4}{6}$ B. $\frac{7}{14}$ C. $\frac{5}{15}$ **25.** A. $\frac{10}{16}$ B. $\frac{28}{32}$ C. $\frac{15}{40}$

26. A. $\frac{24}{32}$ B. $\frac{12}{18}$ C. $\frac{14}{16}$ **27.** A. $\frac{30}{45}$ B. $\frac{20}{32}$ C. $\frac{27}{30}$ **28.** A. $\frac{14}{42}$ B. $\frac{15}{20}$ C. $\frac{16}{24}$

▰▰▰Practice

Choose a calculator, paper and pencil, or mental math. Determine whether each pair of ratios forms a proportion.

1. $\frac{8}{9}, \frac{4}{3}$

2. $\frac{20}{16}, \frac{18}{15}$

3. $\frac{18}{12}, \frac{21}{14}$

4. $\frac{21}{27}, \frac{35}{45}$

_____ _____ _____ _____

5. $\frac{18}{22}, \frac{45}{55}$

6. $\frac{38}{52}, \frac{57}{80}$

7. $\frac{10}{65}, \frac{18}{87}$

8. $\frac{51}{48}, \frac{68}{64}$

_____ _____ _____ _____

Find the value of each variable.

9. $\frac{4}{5} = \frac{x}{15}$

10. $\frac{8}{m} = \frac{4}{15}$

11. $\frac{39}{27} = \frac{26}{m}$

12. $\frac{y}{5} = \frac{32}{20}$

_____ _____ _____ _____

13. $\frac{14}{b} = \frac{8}{12}$

14. $\frac{a}{18} = \frac{16}{24}$

15. $\frac{d}{25} = \frac{12}{15}$

16. $\frac{28}{42} = \frac{26}{x}$

_____ _____ _____ _____

17. $\frac{16}{24} = \frac{y}{27}$

18. $\frac{50}{8} = \frac{x}{25}$

19. $\frac{9}{10} = \frac{c}{45}$

20. $\frac{x}{90} = \frac{45}{50}$

_____ _____ _____ _____

Solve each problem.

21. In the 1991-92 National Basketball Association Championship games, the Chicago Bulls won 2 games for each game that the Portland Trailblazers won. If Portland won 2 games, how many did Chicago win? _____

Source: World Almanac and Book of Facts

22. In 1915, there was one divorce for every 1,000 people in the United States. If a certain town had a population of 56,000 people, how many divorces would you have expected in that town? _____

Source: World Almanac and Book of Facts

23. For every 100 families with TV sets, about 12 families like *Star Trek, the Next Generation.* In a town of 23,400 families who all have TV sets, how many families would you expect to like *Star Trek, the Next Generation?* _____

Source: World Almanac and Book of Facts

24. In 1800, there were only about 6 people per square mile of land in the U.S. What was the approximate population in 1800 if there were about 364,700 square miles in the U.S.?

Source: Almanac and Book of Facts, Source listed there: Bureau of the Census

Practice

Use guess and test to solve each problem.

1. A deli sells ham sandwiches for $2 and roast beef sandwiches for $3. A committee organizing a family reunion placed orders for 85 sandwiches. The bill came to $218, before tax. How many ham sandwiches were ordered?

_____

2. Tickets for a community dinner cost $4 for adults and $3 for children. A total of 390 tickets were sold, earning $1,380. How many of each type of ticket were sold?

_____

3. Place the digits 3, 4, 7, 9, and 12 in the circles at the right so that the product is the same left to right and up and down. What is the product?

_____

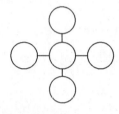

Choose any strategy to solve each problem. Show your work.

4. Two numbers have a sum of 42 and a product of 432. What are the two numbers? _____

5. Two numbers have a sum of 70 and a product of 1,189. What are the numbers? _____

6. Louise, Bill, and Fran each had a different piece of fruit packed in their lunches. A apple, an orange, and a banana were packed. Louise won't eat apples. Bill is allergic to oranges. Fran eats only bananas. What piece of fruit did each person have?

_____

_____

7. A train ride at an amusement park opens at 10:00 A.M. and closes at 7:00 P.M. The train has 6 cars. Each car seats 24 people. Tickets cost $2 for adults and $1 for children. The ride is 45 min long. Last Saturday, the amusement park was crowded, and the train always ran filled to capacity. Records show that there were twice as many children as there were adult riders that day. How much money did the train ride earn that day? _____

8. The floor plan of the first floor of a museum is shown at the right. If you enter at A, is it possible to go through each doorway only one time, see each room, and exit at B? If this can be done, show how. You may enter each room more than one time.

_____

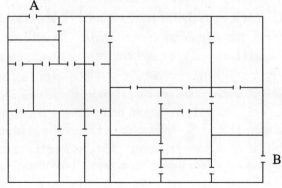

Practice

Write the letter of the figure that appears to be similar to each given figure.

1. A _____
2. B _____
3. E _____
4. I _____
5. J _____

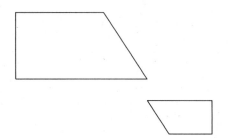

6. Draw two rectangles that are similar. Label the vertices and the dimensions.

7. Draw two trapezoids that are similar. Label the vertices and the dimensions.

Trace and cut out the figures below. For each pair, lay the smaller figure over the larger figure and compare them. Which pairs are similar figures? _____

8.

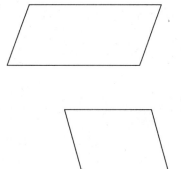

9.

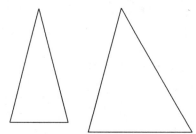

10.

11.

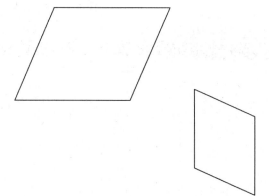

Practice

Use the scale for each drawing to determine the actual
size of each line.

1.

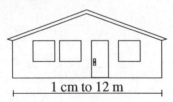

1 cm to 12 m

_____

2.

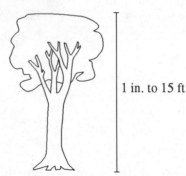

1 in. to 15 ft

_____

3.

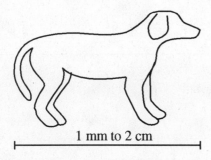

1 in. to 6 ft

_____

4.

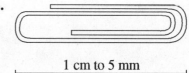

1 cm to 5 mm

_____

5.

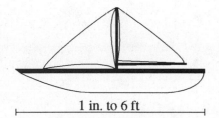

1 mm to 2 cm

_____

6.

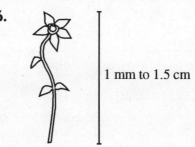

1 mm to 1.5 cm

_____

7. Find the measure in cm of your thumb from the tip of your
fingernail to where it meets your wrist. If you drew a $\frac{3}{4}$-size
picture of yourself, how long would your thumb be in the
drawing? _____

8. The length of a wall in a floorplan is $6\frac{1}{2}$ in. The actual wall
is 78 ft long. Find the scale of the floorplan. _____

9. The height of a building is $3\frac{3}{8}$ in. on a scale drawing.
Find the actual height of the building if the scale used is
$\frac{3}{4}$ in. : 2 ft. _____

▰▰▰Practice

Use the 10 × 10 grid to model each percent.

1. 72%

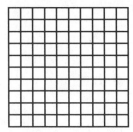

2. 14%

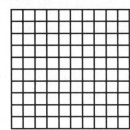

3. 34%

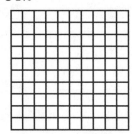

4. 56%

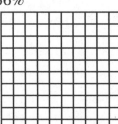

5. 5%

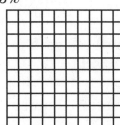

6. 11%

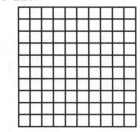

Write each as a percent.

7. 37 students out of 100 students have blue eyes. _____

8. 3 light bulbs per every 100 light bulbs were found to be defective. ____

9. 92 yes votes out of 100 votes _____

10. 29 students out of 100 students live in an apartment. _____

For Exercises 11–13, use the whole numbers 1 through 100.

11. What percent of the numbers are even numbers? _____

12. What percent of the numbers are multiples of 6? _____

13. What percent of the numbers are multiples of 8? _____

14. A human's brain makes up about 2% of his or her body weight. What is the approximate weight of the brain of a person who weighs 100 lb? _____

15. Approximately 65% of a person's body weight is water. Merga's aunt weighs 100 lb. How many pounds are water? _____

16. Sixteen percent of the seventh-graders at East Side School chose art as an after-school interest. What percent of the students did not choose art? _____

▬▬▬Practice

Write each fraction as a decimal and as a percent.

1. $\frac{3}{5}$ _____ **2.** $\frac{7}{10}$ _____ **3.** $\frac{13}{25}$ _____ **4.** $\frac{17}{20}$ _____

Write each decimal as a percent and as a fraction in simplest form.

5. 0.02 _____ **6.** 0.45 _____ **7.** 0.4 _____ **8.** 0.92 _____

Write each percent as a decimal and as a fraction in simplest form.

9. 46% _____ **10.** 17% _____ **11.** 90% _____ **12.** 5% _____

The table shows the fraction of students who participated in extracurricular activities from 1960 to 1990. Complete the table by writing each fraction as a percent.

Students' Extracurricular Choices

Year	1960	1965	1970	1975	1980	1985	1990
Student participation (fraction)	$\frac{3}{4}$	$\frac{8}{10}$	$\frac{17}{20}$	$\frac{39}{50}$	$\frac{21}{25}$	$\frac{19}{25}$	$\frac{87}{100}$
Student participation (percent)	——	——	——	——	——	——	——

Write each fraction or decimal as a percent. Write the percent (without the percent sign) in the puzzle.

Across

1. $\frac{3}{5}$

2. $\frac{1}{5}$

3. 0.55

5. 0.23

6. $\frac{7}{20}$

7. 0.17

9. 0.4

10. $\frac{9}{25}$

Down

1. $\frac{13}{20}$

2. 0.25

3. $\frac{1}{2}$

4. $\frac{3}{20}$

5. 0.24

6. $\frac{3}{10}$

7. 0.1

8. $\frac{4}{25}$

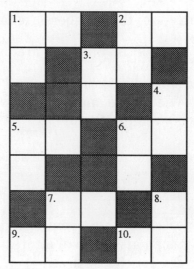

███████ **Practice**

Estimate each of the following amounts. Hint: draw a model.

1. 81% of $600 _____   **2.** 20% of $4.90 _____   **3.** 48% of 500 _____

Circle A, B, C, or D. Determine the best estimate.

4. 72% of 80
  A. 64   **B.** 56
  C. 6   **D.** 5.6

5. 18% of 90
  A. 18   **B.** 9
  C. 27   **D.** 15

6. 21% of 80
  A. 20   **B.** 160
  C. 16   **D.** 16.8

7. 39% of 200
  A. 80   **B.** 60
  C. 100   **D.** 72

8. 81% of 150
  A. 80   **B.** 120
  C. 160   **D.** 60

9. 68% of 250
  A. 140   **B.** 210
  C. 170   **D.** 175

Solve.

10. A real estate agent receives a 9% commission for every house sold. Suppose she sold a house for $112,000. Estimate her commission. _____

11. Mr. Andropolis wants to leave the waitress a 12% tip. Estimate the tip he should leave if the family's bill is $32.46.

   _____

12. A shoe store is having a sale. Boots are marked down 20%. Estimate the savings on a pair of boots regularly priced at $57.99. _____

13. Michael receives a 9.8% annual raise. He currently earns $1,789.46 per month. Estimate the amount by which his monthly earnings will increase.

   _____

14. Estimate the sales tax and final cost of a book that costs $12.95 with a sales tax of 6%.

   _____

15. Three stores are having a sale on running shoes. Which sale has the greatest savings? _____

   a. 20% of 32.98   **b.** 15% of $40.00   **c.** 25% of $24.50

Practice

Find each percent.

1. 15% of 20 _____

2. 40% of 80 _____

3. 20% of 45 _____

4. 18% of 70 _____

5. 90% of 120 _____

6. 65% of 700 _____

7. 25% of 84 _____

8. 63% of 80 _____

9. 60% of 50 _____

10. 45% of 90 _____

11. 12% of 94 _____

12. 15% of 52 _____

13. 37% of 80 _____

14. 25% of 16 _____

15. 63% of 800 _____

16. 72% of 950 _____

17. 55% of 250 _____

18. 18% of 420 _____

19. 33% of 140 _____

20. 53% of 400 _____

21. The Badgers won 75% of their 32 games this year. How many games did they win? _____

22. Vivian earned $540 last month. She saved 30% of this money. How much did she save? _____

23. A survey of the students at Lakeside School yielded the results shown below. There are 1,400 students enrolled at Lakeside. Complete the table for the number of students in each activity.

How Lakeside Students Spend Their Time on Saturday

Activity	Percent of Students	Number of Students
Babysitting	22%	
Sports	26%	
Job	15%	
At home	10%	
Tutoring	10%	
Other	17%	

◼◼◼▬▬ *Practice*

Display the data in a circle graph.

1. Ms. Murphy's Class's Favorite Foods

Pizza	Spaghetti	Hamburger
60%	30%	10%

2. Mr. Chung's Class's Favorite Type of Book

Animal	Sports	Adventure	Mystery
20%	25%	10%	45%

3. Mr. Fano's Class's Favorite Color

Blue	Purple	Red
40%	35%	25%

4. Ms. Ramon's Class's Favorite Sport

Swimming	Softball	Soccer	Hockey
20%	30%	5%	45%

5. Number of TV Stations Received By Homes

1–6	7–10	11–14	15–40	41–60
7%	34%	34%	19%	6%

6. Tom Pin's Bowling Record

Games Won	Games Lost	Games Tied	Forfeits
50%	35%	5%	10%

Practice

Mirga and José played a game and completed the table below.

Mirga wins	ⅢⅢ ⅢⅢ ⅢⅢ ⅢⅢ ⅢⅢ Ⅰ
José wins	ⅢⅢ Ⅰ
Times played	ⅢⅢ ⅢⅢ ⅢⅢ ⅢⅢ ⅢⅢ ⅢⅢ ⅠⅠ

1. Find Probability(Mirga wins) and Probability(José wins).

   _____

2. Do you think the game is fair? Explain.

   _____

   _____

Andy and Bryan are playing a game in which Andy wins if the sum of the numbers on 2 number cubes is even, and Bryan wins if the sum of the numbers is odd.

3. Complete the grid at the right.

4. What sum appears most often?

   _____

5. How many outcomes are even numbers?

   _____

6. How many outcomes are odd numbers?

   _____

+	1	2	3	4	5	6
1						
2						
3						
4						
5						
6						

7. Is the game they are playing fair or unfair? _____

8. Nick and Pat are playing a game with a black and white spinner like the one at the right. Nick wins if the spinner stops on black, and Pat wins if it stops on white. Is the game fair or unfair? Explain.

   _____

9. Draw two spinners. Make and label one fair and the other unfair.

Practice

Simulate and solve each problem. Show all your work.

Marty makes 60% of his free throws.

1. a. What is the probability that he will make two free throws in a row? Draw a spinner to represent his free throw percent. Use the circle at the right. _____

_____

b. Marty practices and can now make 80% of his free throws. Draw a spinner to represent his free throw percent. Use the circle at the right.

2. Mail is delivered between 12:00 P.M. and 1:00 P.M. every day to Joe's house. Joe comes home for lunch at 11:30 A.M. for 45 min. What is the probability that the mail will arrive during Joe's lunch break? Draw a spinner to represent the times that the mail is delivered. _____

Use any strategy to solve each problem. Show all your work.

3. You have several coins that total 38 cents. You have the same number of pennies as nickels. How many coins do you have?

_____

A group of 50 middle school students were surveyed about their after school activities. There were 33 students who take dance lessons, 31 students who take music lessons, and 31 students who play organized sports. There are 11 students who do all three activities. Of these 50 students, 5 students only take dance and play sports, 6 students only take music and and play sports, and 12 students only take dance and music.

4. How many take only dance lessons? _____

5. How many take only music lessons? _____

6. How many only play sports? _____

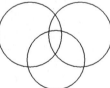

7. There were 10 people at a party. At the end of the party, each person shook hands with each of the others. How many hand shakes were there in all? _____

Practice

Use this list of Random Digits for Exercises 1–4.

62 31 32 64 55 43 63 11 41 34 24 51 14 15 26 32 22 41 26 31
23 41 63 24 11 25 34 52 22 51 42 63 52 32 43 41 11 24 12 33

1. How likely are different digits when you toss two number cubes?

   _____

   _____

2. Find the number of pairs with different digits.

   _____

3. Find the number of times the cubes were tossed.

   _____

4. Find Probability(different digits).

   _____

5. Complete the table. Show the possible numbers formed by the numbers on the faces when two number cubes are tossed.

	1	2	3	4	5	6
1						
2						
3						
4						
5						
6						

6. How many numbers with two different digits were formed in the table for Exercise 5? _____

7. How many possible numbers are there? _____

8. Find Probability (numbers with different digits) as a percent.

   _____

Use the list of Random Digits below for Exercise 9.

1 1 2 1 1 1 2 1 2 1 1 1 1 2 2 2 1 1 1 1 2 2 1 2 2
1 2 2 2 1 1 1 1 1 2 1 1 2 2 1 2 1 1 2 2 2 2 1 1 2
2 2 2 2 2 2 1 1 1 1 1 1 2 1 2 2 1 2 2 1 1 2 1 2 1

9. Suppose 1 represents a coin toss landing heads. How many times would the result of a toss be heads in the first 50 trials?

   _____

▰▰▰▰Practice

A number cube is rolled once. Find each probability. Write as a fraction, decimal, and percent.

1. Probability(even) _____

2. Probability(*not* 3) _____

3. Probability(1, 3, or 5) _____

4. Probability(0) _____

5. Probability(1 or 6) _____

6. Probability(less than 7) _____

Use the spinner at the right.

7. Find Probability(white) as a fraction, decimal, and percent.

   _____

8. Find Probability(black) as a fraction, decimal, and percent.

   _____

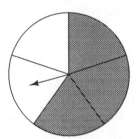

The fund-raising committee sold 500 raffle tickets. Tyrone bought three tickets. There will be one winning ticket.

9. What is the probability that Tyrone will win? _____

10. What is the probability that Tyrone will not win?

    _____

A box contains blue marbles and yellow marbles. Probability(yellow) = $\frac{5}{12}$

11. What is Probability(blue)? _____

12. **Choose A, B, or C.** Which spinner could you use to simulate the problem? _____

    A. 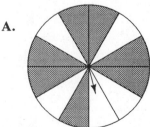   B. 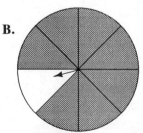   C.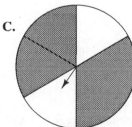

13. If the box contains 24 marbles, how many of each color are there?

    _____

▬▬▬Practice

Each shape in a set of attribute blocks comes in two sizes (small and large), three colors (yellow, red, and blue), and two thicknesses (thick and thin).

1. Use a tree diagram and list all the different blocks for each shape.

2. How many outcomes are possible?

   _____

3. Find Probability(red)

   _____

4. How many outcomes will be blue and thin? _____

5. How many outcomes will be large?

   _____

6. Show how you could use the counting principle to find the number of outcomes. _____

7. Suppose a medium size is also available. What is the new total outcomes? _____

Each day Jake makes his lunch for school. Today he can choose from white, rye, or wheat bread. He can choose turkey, cheese, or ham slices.

8. Draw a tree diagram to show all possible sandwiches.

9. How many sandwich choices would he have if lettuce were an option? _____

Marguerite has socks in 4 different colors (red, blue, white, and black) and shoes in 3 different colors (blue, white, and black).

10. What is the probability that she will choose white socks and white shoes? _____

11. What is the probability that she will choose matching socks and shoes? _____

Practice

Use the spinner at the right for Exercises 1–5. It is spun twice.

1. Use multiplication to find the probability that the first spin is white and the second spin is black. _____

black / red

white / black

2. Draw a tree diagram to show all possible outcomes.

3. Find the probability that the two spins different colors. _____

4. Find the probability that the two spins are the same color. _____

5. Are the spins independent events? Explain

_____

6. Roll a die. Find Probability(4). _____

7. The die is rolled again. Find Probability(4). _____

8. Find the probability of rolling 5 two times in a row. _____

9. Find the probability of rolling two 4s in a row. _____

A coin is tossed four times.

10. Find Probability(HTHT). _____

Suppose each letter of your first name is printed on a separate card and put into Container 1.

11. One card is drawn from the container. Find Probability(first letter of your first name). _____

12. Suppose each letter of your last name is printed on a separate card and put into Container 2. One card is drawn from the container. Find Probability(first letter of your last name).

_____

13. One card is drawn from each container. Find Probability(your initials). _____

Practice

1. Make an organized list of how Ali, Ben, and Chou can sit behind each other in a row.

2. Make an organized list of all possible arrangements of the letters in the word BITE. How many of the arrangements are English words? _____

3. Mrs. Schoup has three errands to do on her way home from work.

   a. Draw a tree diagram to show all the different arrangements of going to the post office, the library, and the gas station.

   b. How many different ways can Ms. Schoup organize her errands? _____

4. Vince has homework in math, science, language, and reading. How many different ways can he do his homework?

   _____

5. The spring program will feature songs from five grade levels. How many different ways can these grade levels be arranged?

   _____

6. How many different ways can six posters be displayed side-by-side? _____

7. Amy can scramble the letters in her name and make two more words. How many different ways can the letters in her name be scrambled into nonwords? _____

8. How many different ways can you scramble the letters in your first name? _____

9. Can you make any different words from the letters in your first name? _____

Practice

Answer each question in a complete sentence in your own words.

1. What is a population? _____

   _____

   _____

2. What is a sample? _____

   _____

   _____

3. When is a sample random? _____

   _____

   _____

4. Why must a sample be representative of the whole population?

   _____

   _____

For Exercises 5–7, state whether the sample is random. Explain.

5. The library plans to increase its hours of operation. For a two-week period, it is surveying each patron who checks out books.

   _____

   _____

   _____

6. A traffic signal is being considered at a certain intersection. A mechanical counter records the time and number of vehicles from 6:00 A.M. to 9:00 P.M. for one week.

   _____

   _____

   _____

7. A book publisher wants to know the opinions of 12-year-olds in a school district. The name of each 12-year-old is placed in a bin and 20 names are chosen.

   _____

   _____

   _____

Practice

1. Graph these integers on the number line: –4, 9, 1, –2, 3.

Name the integer that is represented by each point.

2. *J* _____

3. *K* _____

4. *L* _____

5. *M* _____

Write an integer to represent each situation.

6. spent $23 _____

7. lost 12 yards _____

8. deposit of $58 _____

Name the opposite of each integer.

9. 16 _____

10. –12 _____

11. 100 _____

12. 75 _____

Compare using <, >, or =.

13. –5 ☐ 8

14. 13 ☐ –14

15. –11 ☐ –19

Write an integer between the given integers.

16. –2, 9 _____

17. 3, –12 _____

18. –7, –11 _____

Complete with an integer that makes each statement true.

19. –9 > _____

20. _____ > 3

21. 0 > _____

22. List the temperatures from least to greatest. _____

- The temperature was 25°F below zero.
- The pool temperature was 78°F.
- Water freezes at 32°F.
- The low temperature in December is –3°F.
- The temperature in the refrigerator was 34°F.

Think of the days of a week as integers. Let today be 0, and let days in the past be negative and days in the future be positive.

23. If today is Tuesday, what integer stands for last Sunday? _____

24. If today is Wednesday, what integer stands for next Saturday? _____

25. If today is Friday, what integer stands for last Saturday? _____

26. If today is Monday, what integer stands for next Monday? _____

▬▬▬Practice

**Write the integer that is represented by the tiles.
Unshaded tiles represent positive integers and shaded
tiles represent negative integers.**

1. _____

2. _____

3. _____

4. _____

5. _____

6. _____

7. _____

8. _____

9. _____

**Shade the given tiles to represent each integer in two
ways. Use unshaded tiles for positive integers and shaded
tiles for negative integers.**

10. –4
   a. ▢▢▢▢
   b. ▢▢▢▢▢▢
      ▢▢

11. 5
   a. ▢▢▢▢▢
   b. ▢▢▢▢▢▢
      ▢▢▢▢▢

12. 7
   a. ▢▢▢▢▢▢▢
   b. ▢▢▢▢▢▢▢▢
      ▢

13. –8
   a. ▢▢▢▢▢▢▢▢
   b. ▢▢▢▢▢▢▢▢
      ▢▢▢▢

14. 2
   a. ▢▢
   b. ▢▢▢▢▢
      ▢▢▢▢▢

15. –9
   a. ▢▢▢▢▢▢▢▢▢
   b. ▢▢▢▢▢▢▢
      ▢▢▢▢▢▢

Shade the tiles to represent the given integer.

16. 4
   ▢▢▢▢▢▢▢▢

17. –3
   ▢▢▢▢▢▢▢▢▢▢▢

18. –6
   ▢▢▢▢▢▢▢▢▢▢▢▢

19. 0
   ▢▢▢▢▢▢▢▢▢▢

20. Draw models of all posible integers that can be represented
    using 4 tiles.

   ▢▢▢▢   ▢▢▢▢   ▢▢▢▢   ▢▢▢▢   ▢▢▢▢

   _____   _____   _____   _____   _____

Practice

Write a numerical expression for each model. Find the sum.

1. _____

2. _____

3. _____

Use tiles to find each sum.

4. $-2 + (-8)$ _____

5. $8 + (-4)$ _____

6. $-6 + 3$ _____

7. $6 + (-4)$ _____

8. $-1 + 7$ _____

9. $-8 + 3$ _____

10. $-2 + (-6)$ _____

11. $6 + (-9)$ _____

12. $-5 + (-7)$ _____

13. $-4 + (-7)$ _____

14. $4 + (-7)$ _____

15. $-4 + 7$ _____

Compare. Write <, >, or =.

16. $-5 + (-6)$ ☐ $6 + (-5)$

17. $-8 + 10$ ☐ $-3 + 6$

18. $-4 + (-9)$ ☐ $-8 + (-5)$

19. $20 + (-12)$ ☐ $-12 + (-4)$

Solve.

20. Bill has overdrawn his account by $15. There is a $10 service charge for an overdrawn account. If he deposits $60, what is his new balance? _____

21. Jody deposited $65 into her savings account. The next day, she withdrew $24. How much of her deposit remains in the account? _____

22. The outside temperature at noon was 9°F. The temperature dropped 15 degrees during the afternoon. What was the new temperature? _____

23. The temperature was 10° below zero and dropped 24 degrees. What is the new temperature? _____

24. The high school football team lost 4 yd on one play and gained 9 yd on the next play. What is the total change in yards? _____

25. Philip earned $5 for shoveling snow, $2 for running errands, and received $8 allowance. He spent $6 at the movies and $3 for baseball cards. How much money does he have left?

_____

▬▬▬Practice

Write a numerical expression for each model. Find the difference.

1.  _____

2.  _____

3.  _____

4. _____

Use tiles to find each difference.

5. 2 – 5 _____   **6.** –5 – 2 _____   **7.** –6 – 3 _____

8. 10 – (–3) _____   **9.** –9 – (–2) _____   **10.** 0 – (–5) _____

11. –12 – (–3) _____   **12.** 8 – 13 _____   **13.** 11 – (–6) _____

Compare. Write <, >, or =.

14. 5 – 12 ☐ 5 – (–12)   **15.** 8 – (–5) ☐ –8 – 5

16. 9 – (–4) ☐ 4 – (–9)   **17.** –12 – 12 ☐ 12 – (–12)

Evaluate each expression when $a = -3$, $b = -4$, and $c = 5$.

18. 9 – a _____   **19.** c – b _____   **20.** –20 – c _____

21. b – a _____   **22.** c – 16 _____   **23.** –14 – a _____

Solve.

24. The temperature was 48°F and dropped 15° in two hours. What was the temperature after the change? _____

25. The temperature at midnight is –5°C and is expected to drop 12° by sunrise. What is the expected temperature at sunrise? _____

26. Catherine has $400 in her checking account. Her utility bills total $600. How much more money does she need to pay the utility bills? _____

27. On the first play, the football team lost 6 yd. On the second play, the team lost 5 yd. What was their total change in yards? _____

28. Use the thermometer to find the final reading at 2 P.M. _____

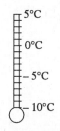

10 A.M.	reading of 5°C
11 A.M.	drops 5°C
12 noon	drops 3°C
1 P.M.	drops 4°C
2 P.M.	rises 5°C

Practice

Use any strategy to solve each problem. Show all your work.

1. Sticker numbers are available at hardware stores or craft stores. You need to number 100 lockers from 1 to 100 with the sticker numbers. Which digit will be used the least number of times? the most? _____

2. Commuter trains pass through the station every half hour from 6 A.M. through 7 P.M. How many trains pass through the station each day? _____

3. Bonnie is older than Will and younger than Jean. Katie is older than Will. Bonnie is younger than Peggy. Jean is older than Katie and younger than Megan. Katie is older than Bonnie. Who is the youngest? _____

4. Seven schools will play each other in a soccer tournament. How many games need to be played? _____

5. Arrange the digits 0, 1, 2, 3, 4, 5, 6, 7, 8, and 9 to form two five-digit numbers so that the difference is as large as possible.

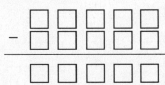

6. Weekend admission charges at the zoo are $3.50 for adults, $1.50 for seniors, and $2.00 for children (5–12 years old). Children under 5 are admitted free. The parking fee is $3.00. What is the total cost for a group of four adults, two seniors, and children with ages 3, 4, 5, 6, 7, 8, 9, 10, 11, and 12 that came in three cars? _____

7. Al went shopping and spent half his money and $5 more at a gift shop. At the food store, he spent half his remaining money and $5 more. He had only $2.50 left. How much money did Al have when he went into the gift shop?

   _____

8. The last Friday of last month was the 26th day of the month. What day of the week was the first day of last month?

   _____

9. How many calls will be made among six people if each person needs to talk to each of the other people one time?

   _____

▰▰▰ Practice

Name the point with the given coordinates.

1. (2, 3) _____   2. (−4, 0) _____

3. (−3, −5) _____   4. (0, 6) _____

5. (3, 5) _____   6. (4, 0) _____

Write the coordinates of each point.

7. *J* _____   8. *E* _____

9. *D* _____   10. *A* _____

11. *G* _____   12. *C* _____

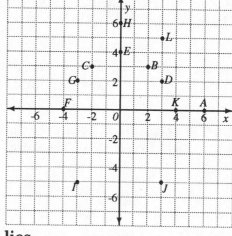

Identify the quadrant in which each point lies.

13. (8, −4) _____   14. (−4, 8) _____   15. (4, 8) _____

16. (−8, −4) _____   17. (8, 4) _____   18. (−4, −8) _____

Use the coordinate plane below.

19. Graph four points on the coordinate plane so that when the points are connected in order, the shape is a rectangle.

_____

20. Graph four points on the coordinate plane so that when the points are connected in order, the shape is a parallelogram that is not a rectangle.

_____

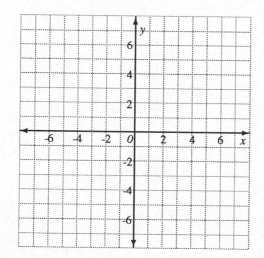

Practice

Use the graph at the right.

1. Translate point *A* down 3 units. What are its new coordinates?

   _____

2. Translate point *B* up 2 units and to the left 2 units. What are its new coordinates?

   _____

3. Point *C* is translated to point *F*. How far and in which directions has point *C* moved?

   _____

4. Reflect point *D* across the *y*-axis. What are its new coordinates?

   _____

5. Reflect point *E* across the *x*-axis and across the *y*-axis. What are its new coordinates?

   _____

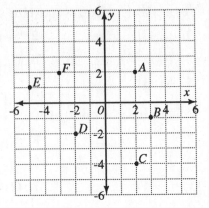

6. Translate the figure 5 units to the left and 4 units up.

7. Name the coordinates of the vertices of the new figure.

   _____

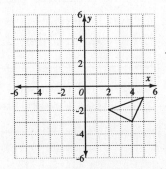

8. Reflect the figure across the *x*-axis.

9. Name the coordinates of the vertices of the new figure.

   _____

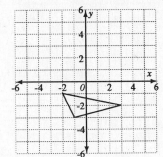

Practice

What scale and intervals would you use to graph each data set?

1. 5, –9, 18, –6, 12, 16   _____

2. –13, 8, –10, 5, 9, 2   _____

3. –45, 40, –16, –8, –26, 32   _____

4. –10, –26, 18, 11, 3, –2   _____

Choose a calculator, mental math, or paper and pencil.

5. –18 + 7 _____   **6.** 16 – 37 _____   **7.** 326 + (–326) _____

8. 43 – (–18) _____   **9.** 1,258 + (–271) _____   **10.** –73 + (–92) _____

11. Find the closing balance for each day.

Day	Expenses	Income	Balance
Sunday	–$32	$45	
Monday	–$40	$50	
Tuesday	–$26	$40	
Wednesday	–$50	$45	
Thursday	–$35	$30	
Friday	–$70	$60	
Saturday	–$53	$60	

12. Draw a line graph to display the balances in Exercise 11.

13. On which day did the greatest gain occur? _____

14. On which day did the greatest loss occur? _____

15. What was the total balance for the week? Was it a loss or profit?

_____

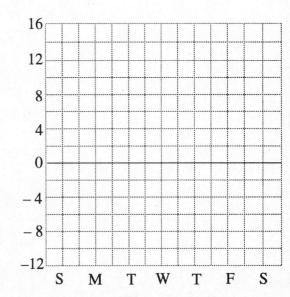

Chapter 1 Cumulative Review

Choose the best answer. Circle A, B, C, or D.

1. Find two numbers that have a sum of 45 and a product of 450.

   A. 10, 35   **B.** 20, 25
   C. 12, 33   **D.** 15, 30

2. Find the product of 37 × 55.

   A. 1,925   **B.** 2,037
   C. 2,035   **D.** 3,035

3. Find the sum of 55 + 64 + 36 + 40.

   A. 195   **B.** 200
   C. 100   **D.** 155

4. Find the quotient of 654 ÷ 6.

   A. 118   **B.** 3,924
   C. 55   **D.** 109

5. Find the difference of 63,540 − 7,641.

   A. 55,800   **B.** 55,799
   C. 55,899   **D.** 71,181

6. Carlita has 8 coins that total $.58. How many dimes does she have?

   A. 0 dimes   **B.** 1 dime
   C. 2 dimes   **D.** 3 dimes

7. Find two consecutive integers whose product is 156.

   A. 13, 14   **B.** 12, 13
   C. 2, 78   **D.** 6, 26

8. According to the circle graph shown, what is the most preferred way to prepare eggs?

   Preferred Preparation of Eggs

   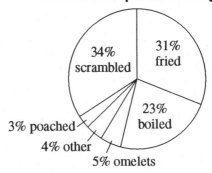

   A. fried   **B.** scrambled
   C. boiled   **D.** omelets

9. What is the total percentage that do not like their eggs fried or scrambled?

   A. 4%   **B.** 12%
   C. 23%   **D.** 35%

10. In the pasture on his grandfather's farm, Mark counted 80 legs and 25 animals. There were only cows and egrets in the pasture. How many cows were there in the pasture?

   A. 10 cows   **B.** 15 cows
   C. 20 cows   **D.** 25 cows

11. Find the range of the following set of numbers.
   56, 62, 55, 57, 56, 63, 56, 58, 60, 62

   A. 63 − 55   **B.** 56
   C. 10   **D.** 13

Chapter 1 Cumulative Review (continued)

12. Which of the following line plots represent the data from Exercise 11?

A.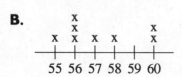

B.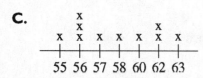

C.

D.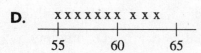

13. Find the mean of the following data.
37, 45, 50, 35, 41, 43, 54, 41, 38, 46

    A. 10   **B.** 41

    C. 42   **D.** 43

14. Find the median of the data in Exercise 13.

    A. 10   **B.** 41

    C. 42   **D.** 43

15. Find the mode of the data in Exercise 13.

    A. 10   **B.** 41

    C. 42   **D.** 43

16. Riki works a summer job for $4.82 an hour. The following spreadsheet entry is a typical work week. How much does she earn in a typical week?

	A	B	C	D	E
1	Day	Time In	Time Out	Total Hours	Amount Earned
2	Sat.	1	6		
3	Mon.	2	8		
4	Tues.	2	8		
5	Wed.	1	8		
6	Thurs.	1	8		
7			Weekly Total		

    A. $149.42   **B.** $144.60

    C. $154.24   **D.** $168.70

17. What would not be a formula for finding out how much she earned in a week?

    A. E7 = E2 + E3 + E4 + E5 + E6

    B. E7 = 4.82 * D7

    C. E7 = (D2 + D3 + D4 + D5 + D6) * 4.82

    D. E7 = (E2 + E3 + E4 + E5 + E6) * 4.82

18. How many weeks will she have to save in order to take a $744.00 one-week trip to Disneyland?

    A. about 4 weeks   **B.** about 5 weeks

    C. about 6 weeks   **D.** about 7 weeks

Chapter 2 Cumulative Review

Choose the best answer. Circle A, B, C, or D.

1. Find the sum of
356 + 444 + 23 + 117.

   A. 920   **B.** 940

   C. 1040   **D.** 930

2. Find the product 26×6.

   A. 126   **B.** 166

   C. 156   **D.** 136

**Use the table below to answer
Exercises 3–5.**

Number on Die	Tally
1	卌 ||||
2	卌 ||
3	卌 卌
4	卌 |||
5	卌 |
6	卌 卌

3. How many times was the die thrown?

   A. 10   **B.** 50

   C. 21   **D.** 30

4. What was the greatest number of
times a number on the die was seen?

   A. 6   **B.** 20

   C. 10   **D.** 4

5. What number on the die was seen the
least number of times?

   A. 5   **B.** 3

   C. 2   **D.** 6

6. Find the difference $24{,}000 - 438$.

   A. 23,562   **B.** 24,438

   C. 23,672   **D.** 22,562

**Use the figure below to answer
Exercises 7–10.**

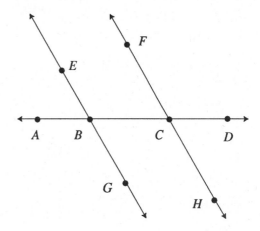

7. Which are noncollinear points?

   A. A, B, D **B.** E, B, G

   C. F, C, H **D.** A, G, F

8. Which angles appear to be obtuse?

   A. $\angle ABG, \angle ABE$ **B.** $\angle BCH, \angle BCF$

   C. $\angle FCD, \angle EBC$ **D.** $\angle EBA, \angle FCB$

9. Which are intersecting lines?

   A. $\overleftrightarrow{EG}$ and $\overleftrightarrow{FH}$ **B.** $\overleftrightarrow{EG}$ and $\overleftrightarrow{AD}$

   C. $\overleftrightarrow{EB}$ and $\overleftrightarrow{FC}$ **D.** $\overleftrightarrow{BG}$ and $\overleftrightarrow{CH}$

10. Which angles appear to be acute?

   A. $\angle ABG, \angle BCH$ **B.** $\angle DCH, \angle DCF$

   C. $\angle ABE, \angle ABG$ **D.** $\angle ABE, \angle DCH$

11. Which of the following describes a
scalene triangle?

   A. A triangle with 2 congruent sides

   B. A triangle with 3 congruent sides

   C. A triangle with no congruent sides

   D. A triangle with 4 congruent sides

Chapter 2 Cumulative Review *(continued)*

12. Find the quotient 242 ÷ 11.

  A. 21   **B.** 12

  C. 11   **D.** 22

Use the following information to answer Exercises 13, 14, and 15.

Raj's geography test grades are: 72, 83, 85, 79, and 86. He has one more test in the class to take.

13. What grade does he need to make on the test to get a grade of 83 in the class if the teacher uses the mean to determine class grades?

  A. 83   **B.** 100

  C. 89   **D.** 93

14. What grade does he need to make on the test to get a grade of 83 in the class if the mode is used to determine the class grade?

  A. 83   **B.** 100

  C. 89   **D.** 93

15. What is the range of Raj's test scores?

  A. 72   **B.** 14

  C. 5   **D.** 86

16. Which set of three angles describe an obtuse triangle?

  A. 30°, 60°, 90°   **B.** 90°, 40°, 50°

  C. 25°, 65°, 80°   **D.** 40°, 110°, 30°

Use the figure below to answer Exercises 17–19.

17. Which are *not* chords of circle E?

  A. $\overline{AB}, \overline{AE}$ **B.** $\overline{AB}, \overline{BC}$

  C. $\overline{AD}, \overline{AB}$ **D.** $\overline{BC}, \overline{DC}$

18. Which is an obtuse central angle of circle E?

  A. $\angle AEB$ **B.** $\angle AED$

  C. $\angle DEC$ **D.** $\angle DEA$

19. If the length of $\overline{AC}$ is 20 cm, what is the length of the radius?

  A. 10 cm   **B.** 20 cm

  C. 40 cm   **D.** 15 cm

Choose a Strategy

20. Six students plan to work in pairs on their science projects, but they cannot decide on a partner. Their teacher told Tim, Susan, Anna, Maria, Matt, and Jake to figure out all the different pairs they could make. How many different pairs did they find?

  A. 9   **B.** 3

  C. 15   **D.** 21

Chapter 3 Cumulative Review

Choose the best answer. Circle A, B, C, or D.

1. Find the median of this set of data.
   75, 76, 80, 76, 79, 80, 75, 76

   A. 79   **B.** 76

   C. 75   **D.** 80

2. How many different ways can you combine dimes, nickels, and pennies to make 13 cents?

   A. 4 ways   **B.** 2 ways

   C. 3 ways   **D.** 5 ways

3. How many centimeters is 18.56 meters?

   A. 185.6 cm   **B.** 1.856 cm

   C. 0.1856 cm   **D.** 1,856 cm

4. What is 0.45 in words?

   A. forty-five tenths

   B. forty-five

   C. forty-five hundredths

   D. forty-five thousandths

5. Estimate the cost of the movie and refreshments by rounding to the nearest dollar.
   movie $4.60
   popcorn $2.79
   drink $1.45
   snack $1.23

   A. $9   **B.** $10

   C. $11   **D.** $12

6. Find the difference 35.46 − 22.98.

   A. 58.44   **B.** 12.46

   C. 12.48   **D.** 13.58

Use the diagram below to answer Exercises 7-9.

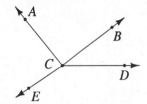

7. Which are rays in the figure?

   A. $\overrightarrow{AB}, \overrightarrow{CD}$ **B.** $\overrightarrow{AB}, \overrightarrow{AE}$

   C. $\overrightarrow{CA}, \overrightarrow{CD}$ **D.** $\overrightarrow{DB}, \overrightarrow{DC}$

8. Which angle appears to be obtuse?

   A. $\angle BCD$ **B.** $\angle ECD$

   C. $\angle ECA$ **D.** $\angle BCA$

9. Which angle appears to be acute?

   A. $\angle BCD$ **B.** $\angle ECD$

   C. $\angle ECA$ **D.** $\angle BCA$

10. Use the circle graph below to find out the favorite ice cream of the class.

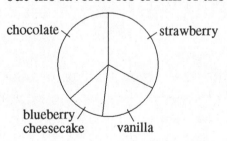

   A. chocolate

   B. vanilla

   C. blueberry cheesecake

   D. strawberry

Chapter 3 Cumulative Review (continued)

11. Use the circle graph in Exercise 10 to find the least favorite ice cream of the class.

    A. chocolate

    B. vanilla

    C. blueberry cheesecake

    D. strawberry

12. Find the mean of Jason's test scores. 90, 81, 95, 79, 89, 93, 92, 93

    A. 91   B. 89

    C. 93   D. 84

13. Which figure is not congruent to the figure below?

    A.   B.

    C.   D.

14. Estimate the sum of an acute angle and a right angle.

    A. less than 90°

    B. more than 180°

    C. equal to 180°

    D. between 90° and 180°

15. Which of the following is *not* true?

    A. 1.03 > 1.02   B. 0.35 < 0.25

    C. 2.33 < 3.22   D. 0.04 > 0.03

16. Find the sum 1.23 + 3.58 + 12.33.

    A. 17.14   B. 18.14

    C. 16.04   D. 17.24

17. Round 12,344.49 to the place of the underlined digit.

    A. 12,350   B. 12,340

    C. 12,345   D. 12,300

18. Find the mode of this set of data. 3, 5, 6, 4, 6, 9, 8, 5, 6, 3, 7, 2, 1

    A. 5   B. 9

    C. 8   D. 6

19. Aaron opened a savings account with a $25.45 deposit. He then deposited $2.25 weekly for three weeks and then spent $6.38. What is his current balance?

    A. $25.45   B. $38.58

    C. $25.08   D. $25.82

20. There were 33 students polled about their type of transportation. Twenty students had bicycles, fifteen had in-line skates, and thirteen had skateboards. Three students that had bicycles also had skateboards but no in-line skates. Two students with bicycles had in-line skates but no skateboards. Two students that had in-line skates also had skateboards but no bicycles. Six students had all three types of transportation. How many had none of the three types of transportation?

    A. 4 students   B. 15 students

    C. 0 students   D. 6 students

Chapter 4 Cumulative Review

Choose the best answer. Circle A, B, C, or D.

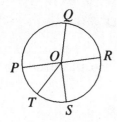

1. Which three points are collinear in circle *O*?

   A. *P, O,* and *S*   **B.** *P, Q,* and *R*

   C. *P, O,* and *R*   **D.** *T, O,* and *S*

2. Name an acute central angle in circle *O*.

   A. ∠*POQ*   **B.** ∠*TOS*

   C. ∠*POR*   **D.** ∠*TOR*

3. If the length of $\overline{QO}$ is 6 cm, what is the diameter of circle *O*?

   A. 12 cm   **B.** 6 cm

   C. 3 cm   **D.** 24 cm

4. Express 2.372 in words.

   A. two and three hundred seventy-two thousandths

   B. two and three hundred seventy-two hundredths

   C. twenty-three and seventy-two hundredths

   D. twenty-three thousand and seventy-two thousandths

5. Which figure does *not* have a line of symmetry?

   A.   **B.**

   C.   **D.**

6. Which set of angles describes an acute triangle?

   A. 90°, 30°, 60°   **B.** 47°, 85°, 48°

   C. 45°, 45°, 90°   **D.** 102°, 60°, 28°

7. Which of the following figures is a rhombus?

   A.    **B.**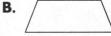

   C. 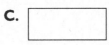   **D.**

8. List the decimals in order from least to greatest.

   0.49, 0.36, 0.23, 0.25, 0.32, 0.54

   A. 0.54, 0.49, 0.36, 0.25, 0.23, 0.32

   B. 0.23, 0.25, 0.32, 0.36, 0.54, 0.49

   C. 0.23, 0.25, 0.32, 0.36, 0.49, 0.54

   D. 0.54, 0.49, 0.36, 0.32, 0.25, 0.23

9. Find the difference $0.94 - 0.27$.

   A. 1.21   **B.** 0.67

   C. 0.77   **D.** 0.73

10. Estimate to the nearest dollar the cost of 4 bottles of juice at $1.18 a bottle and 2 large bags of popcorn at $3.58 a bag.

   A. about $8   **B.** about $10

   C. about $5   **D.** about $12

11. Davis decides to save $2.35 each week from his baby-sitting jobs to buy a present for his father's birthday. If he saves for 5 weeks, how much will he have saved?

   A. $10.55   **B.** $15.00

   C. $11.75   **D.** $12.00

12. To raise money for a new school computer, Jan plans to swim 65 lengths of a 50-m pool. She earns $.10 for every meter she swims. How much money will she raise?

   A. $325   **B.** $3,250

   C. $32.50   **D.** $5.00

13. Which operation would you perform first? $6 \times (5 - 4) + 6 \div 2$

   A. multiplication

   B. division

   C. addition

   D. subtraction

14. What are the missing numbers?
$3 \times (13 - 4) =$
$(\blacksquare \times 13) - (3 \times \blacksquare)$

   A. 3, 13   **B.** 3, −4

   C. −4, 3   **D.** 3, 4

15. Evaluate 5.6×0.9.

   A. 0.504   **B.** 5.04

   C. 56.0   **D.** 50.4

16. Use mental math to find the product $0.034 \times 10,000$.

   A. 340   **B.** 3.40

   C. 34.0   **D.** 3400

17. Find the quotient $8.73 \div 0.3$.

   A. 291   **B.** 29.1

   C. 2.91   **D.** 0.291

18. Use mental math to find the quotient $0.47 \div 1,000$.

   A. 0.00047   **B.** 4.70

   C. 47.0   **D.** 470.0

19. Issa bought four tickets to the county fair for $4.45 each. He paid for the tickets with a twenty-dollar bill. How much change should he receive?

   A. $.20   **B.** $17.80

   C. $4.45   **D.** $2.20

20. Reynold decides to earn extra money by walking dogs after school. He walks dogs for one hour each weekday and charges $3.50 per dog. How much money does he make in one week?

   A. too little information

   B. $24.00

   C. $17.50

   D. $35.00

Chapter 5 Cumulative Review

Choose the best answer. Circle A, B, C, or D.

1. Find the next three terms in the number pattern.
   0, 3, 7, 12, __, __, __
   - **A.** 18, 24, 32
   - **B.** 18, 25, 32
   - **C.** 17, 23, 30
   - **D.** 18, 25, 33

2. Evaluate $4 \times (3^2 + 7)$.
   - **A.** 64
   - **B.** 52
   - **C.** 43
   - **D.** 40

3. Which of the following numbers does *not* round to 18.4?
   - **A.** 18.442
   - **B.** 18.405
   - **C.** 18.4156
   - **D.** 18.4551

4. Of 28 students, four read both *The Red Pony* and *The Hobbit*. Fifteen read the first book, but not the second. Five students read neither book. How many read only *The Hobbit*?
   - **A.** 8 students
   - **B.** 5 students
   - **C.** 4 students
   - **D.** 7 students

5. Which word phrase best describes the expression $x + y$?
   - **A.** a number plus itself
   - **B.** twice a number
   - **C.** a number more than two
   - **D.** a number plus another number

6. Use mental math to solve $k - 4 = 9$.
   - **A.** 5
   - **B.** 9
   - **C.** 13
   - **D.** 36

7. In which equation is the value of y the same as in the equation $y \times 19 = 95$?
   - **A.** $\frac{95}{y} = 5$
   - **B.** $y + 5 = 19$
   - **C.** $\frac{95}{19} = y$
   - **D.** $95 - 19 = y$

8. Which expression is equivalent to $(4 \times 10) + (4 \times 9)$?
   - **A.** 8×19
   - **B.** $4 \times 10 + 9$
   - **C.** $4 \times (10 + 9)$
   - **D.** $8 \times (10 + 9)$

9. Jake measured the length of five pencils. The lengths were 14.6, 14.09, 14.66, 14.69, and 15.1 cm. If Jake orders his measurements from greatest to least, which measurement would be second?
   - **A.** 14.09
   - **B.** 14.69
   - **C.** 14.6
   - **D.** 14.66

10. Find $10.3 - 9.67$.
    - **A.** 6.3
    - **B.** 0.63
    - **C.** 63
    - **D.** 0.063

Name _____ Class _____ Date _____

Chapter 5 Cumulative Review (continued)

11. Use mental math to evaluate $4x - 9$ for $x = 6$.
A. 14 B. 15
C. 33 D. 37

12. Janet used a $20 bill to pay for a tape costing $8.59 and sales tax of $.52. Estimate how much change she will get, rounded to the nearest dollar.
A. $9.00 B. $10.00
C. $11.00 D. $12.00

13. What compatible numbers would you choose to estimate the product 49.46×2.9?
A. 49 and 2 B. 50 and 2
C. 49 and 3 D. 50 and 3

14. Use mental math to evaluate $(2.4 + 8.6) \times 10$.
A. 100 B. 101
C. 110 D. 111

15. Which operations will make the two expressions equal?
$2 + (12 \div 3) = 2 \_ 12 \_ 3$
A. +, + B. −, −
C. ÷, × D. +, ÷

16. In the number 304.097, what is the value of the digit in the hundredths place?
A. 3 B. 4
C. 7 D. 9

17. Evaluate $9 \times 9 - 6 \div 6$.
A. 4.5 B. 12.5
C. 45 D. 80

18. The product of 3.29×1.2 is 3948 without the decimal point. Where should the decimal point be placed?
A. before the 3 B. after the 3
C. after the 9 D. before the 8

19. What do you divide by to change 150 to 0.15?
A. 10 B. 15
C. 100 D. 1,000

Choose a Strategy

20. Ellen bought 8 cans of juice. She gave the clerk $5.00 and received $1.80 in change. Each can of juice costs the same. How much does 1 can of juice cost?
A. $3.20
B. $.40
C. $.60
D. $2.50

© Prentice-Hall, Inc.

Chapter 6 Cumulative Review

Choose the best answer. Circle A, B, C, or D.

1. Evaluate $7.4 - 2.3 \times 2 + 4.8$.

   A. 35   **B.** 34.68

   C. 8   **D.** 7.6

2. Find the product 4.23×0.03.

   A. 0.1269   **B.** 1.269

   C. 0.01269   **D.** 12.69

3. Find the quotient $34.25 \div 0.05$.

   A. 68.5   **B.** 6.85

   C. 0.685   **D.** 685.0

4. If a gallon of regular unleaded gas cost $.989, how much change would you receive from a $20 bill if you bought 12.5 gallons? Round to the nearest cent.

   A. $12.36   **B.** $7.64

   C. $6.90   **D.** $10.00

5. Which expression gives you a value of 92 when you evaluate it?

   A. $35 + 4 \times 15 - 3$

   B. $35 + 4 \times (15 - 3)$

   C. $(35 + 4) \times 15 - 3$

   D. $((35 + 4) \times 15) - 3$

6. Which expression cannot be used to find the area of the figure below?

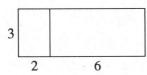

   A. $2 \times 3 + 6 \times 3$

   B. $(2 + 6) \times 3$

   C. $6 + 18$

   D. $2 + (6 \times 3)$

7. Find the perimeter of a square with an area of 16 cm^2.

   A. 8 cm   **B.** 16 cm

   C. 4 cm   **D.** 12 cm

8. Find the perimeter of the figure below.

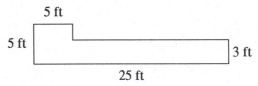

   A. 38 ft   **B.** 40 ft

   C. 60 ft   **D.** 75 ft

9. Find the area of the figure below.

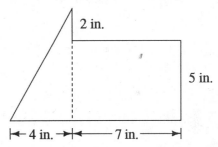

   A. 49 in.^{2} **B.** 43 in.^{2}

   C. 18 in.^{2} **D.** 63 in.^{2}

10. Find the area of the figure below.

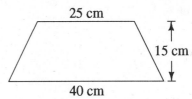

   A. 375 cm^2 **B.** 1,000 cm^2

   C. 600 cm^2 **D.** 487.5 cm^2

Chapter 6 Cumulative Review (continued)

11. A wheel has two circular parts. A black spot is placed on the outside edge of the outside circle and a red spot is placed on the outside edge of the inside circle. The wheel is then rotated 20 times. What is the difference in the distance traveled by the two spots? Use 3.14 for π.

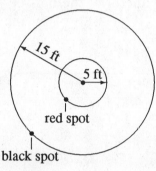

red spot

black spot

A. 0 ft   **B.** 10 ft

C. 628 ft   **D.** 1,256 ft

12. Find the area of the shaded region below. Use 3.14 for π.

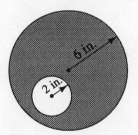

6 in.

2 in.

A. 12.56 in.^{2} **B.** 100.48 in.^{2}

C. 113.04 in.^{2} **D.** 125.6 in.^{2}

13. How many edges does the figure below have?

A. 9 edges   **B.** 8 edges

C. 6 edges   **D.** 5 edges

14. Find the surface area of a rectangular prism with a volume of 60 cm^3 and a length of 5 cm and width of 4 cm.

A. 3 cm   **B.** 47 cm^2

C. 94 cm^2 **D.** 104 cm^2

15. Kelly baby-sits weekly and earns $3.75 an hour. The spreadsheet below shows a typical weekly schedule for her. What is the formula for finding the hours she worked on Friday?

	A	B	C	D	E
	Day	Time Start	Time Stop	Hours Worked	Amount Earned
1	Day	Time Start	Time Stop	Hours Worked	Amount Earned
2	Sun	3	6		
3	Wed	6	8		
4	Fri	6	10		
5	Sat	7	11		
6			Totals		

A. D4 = B4 − C4

B. D4 = C4 − B4

C. D4 = B4 + C4

D. D3 = C3 − B3

16. How much did Kelly earn on Saturday night?

A. $3.75   **B.** $7.50

C. $11.25   **D.** $15.00

17. What is the formula for finding out how much she earned for the week?

A. E6 = E2 + E3 + E4 + E5

B. D6 = D2 + D3 + D4 + D5

C. D6 = (C6 − B6) × $3.75

D. E6 = 4 × D6

▬▬Chapter 7 Cumulative Review

Choose the best answer. Circle A, B, C, or D.

1. Which statement is true?

   A. Three points are always collinear.

   B. A ray is named with one endpoint and any other point on the ray.

   C. Parallel lines always intersect.

   D. A line segment continues without end in opposite directions.

2. Which angle is obtuse?

   A. 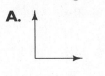   **B.**

   C.   **D.** ←————————→

3. To draw an angle congruent to an ∠ABC, you would

   A. draw an angle half the measure of ∠ABC.

   B. draw an angle the same measure of ∠ABC.

   C. draw an angle twice the measure of ∠ABC.

   D. draw an angle 180° minus the measure of ∠ABC.

4. A polygon with six sides is called a

   A. sixagon   **B.** hexagon

   C. heptagon   **D.** septagon

5. Which figure is *not* congruent to the one below?

   A.   **B.**

   C.   **D.**

6. Which figure would have the most lines of symmetry?

   A. circle   **B.** rectangle

   C. square   **D.** octagon

7. Use Napier's rods to find the product 54,683 × 4.

   A. 109,366   **B.** 164,049

   C. 218,732   **D.** 246,073

8. Use mental math to evaluate $(4 \times 2)^2 - 12$.

   A. 24   **B.** 36

   C. 48   **D.** 52

Chapter 7 Cumulative Review (continued)

9. Which word phrase describes the expression $3x - 15$?

   A. fifteen less than three times a number

   B. fifteen times three less than a number

   C. three less than fifteen times a number

   D. fifteen more than three times a number

10. Solve $12 + n = 21$.

    A. 33   **B.** 12

    C. 9   **D.** 7

11. Solve $24 = m \div 2$.

    A. 6   **B.** 12

    C. 36   **D.** 48

12. Evaluate $3t - s$ for $t = 6$ and $s = 4$.

    A. 18   **B.** 14

    C. 6   **D.** 4

13. Which digit makes $42,\blacksquare52$ divisible by 3 but not divisible by 9?

    A. 2   **B.** 3

    C. 5   **D.** 7

14. Which is the GCF of 54 and 81?

    A. 3   **B.** 6

    C. 9   **D.** 27

15. Which two fractions are equivalent to $\frac{4}{7}$?

    A. $\frac{8}{14}, \frac{16}{21}$ **B.** $\frac{8}{14}, \frac{12}{21}$

    C. $\frac{12}{21}, \frac{32}{40}$ **D.** $\frac{16}{21}, \frac{32}{40}$

16. Write $4\frac{6}{11}$ as an improper fraction.

    A. $\frac{24}{11}$ **B.** $\frac{30}{11}$

    C. $\frac{50}{11}$ **D.** $\frac{10}{11}$

17. The LCM of a number and 14 is 56. Which of the following could be the number?

    A. 8   **B.** 45

    C. 7   **D.** 28

18. Which of the following is *not* true?

    A. $\frac{2}{3} < \frac{7}{4}$ **B.** $1\frac{3}{4} < \frac{13}{8}$

    C. $\frac{2}{5} > \frac{2}{7}$ **D.** $\frac{11}{5} > \frac{13}{7}$

19. Write $\frac{15}{6}$ as a decimal.

    A. 0.25   **B.** 0.5

    C. 2.05   **D.** 2.5

20. You arrived home at 6:30 P.M. one evening after school. You had spent 45 minutes at band practice, 30 minutes at the ice cream shop with friends, 1 hour at the library studying, and 15 minutes riding your bike home. What time did you get out of school?

    A. 3:30 P.M.   **B.** 3:45 P.M.

    C. 4:00 P.M.   **D.** 4:15 P.M.

▬▬▬ Chapter 8 Cumulative Review

Choose the best answer. Circle A, B, C, or D.

1. What is the decimal for twenty-three hundredths?

   A. 23   **B.** 2.3

   C. 0.23   **D.** 0.023

2. List the decimals 0.25, 0.35, 0.23, 0.04, 0.02 from greatest to least.

   A. 0.35, 0.25, 0.23, 0.04, 0.02

   B. 0.04, 0.35, 0.25, 0.23, 0.02

   C. 0.02, 0.04, 0.23, 0.25, 0.35

   D. 0.02, 0.23, 0.04, 0.25, 0.35

3. Find the sum $0.46 + 0.58 + 0.05$.

   A. 0.89   **B.** 1.19

   C. 1.09   **D.** 0.99

4. You have a $10 bill and want to go to the movies for $5.50, buy popcorn for $2.45, and a drink for $1.95. How much change will you get?

   A. none

   B. $.10

   C. $.25

   D. $10 is not enough

5. A spool of thread is 30 m long. What is *not* an equivalent length?

   A. 0.03 km   **B.** 3,000 cm

   C. 30,000 mm   **D.** 0.3 km

6. Find the total area of the pool and deck.

   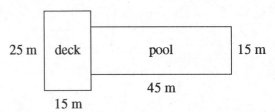

   A. 1,050 m^2 **B.** 675 m^2

   C. 300 m^2 **D.** 375 m^2

7. What is the area of a parallelogram that is 15 ft in height with a base measuring 15 ft?

   A. 25 ft^2 **B.** 30 ft^2

   C. 225 ft^2 **D.** 75 ft^2

8. Find the area of a circle with a circumference of 18.84 ft. Use 3.14 for π.

   A. 28.26 ft^2 **B.** 13.63 ft^2

   C. 56.52 ft^2 **D.** 31.4 ft^2

9. How many vertices does a rectangular prism have?

   A. 10 vertices   **B.** 6 vertices

   C. 4 vertices   **D.** 8 vertices

10. What is the volume of the rectangular prism?

    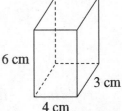

    A. 48 cm^3 **B.** 72 cm^3

    C. 94 cm^3 **D.** 108 cm^3

11. Which is the prime factorization tree of 81?

A.

B.

C.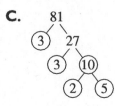

D.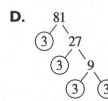

12. What is the GCF of 255 and 170?

A. 5   **B.** 17

C. 10   **D.** 85

13. Write $\frac{35}{60}$ in simplest form.

A. $\frac{35}{60}$ **B.** $\frac{5}{12}$

C. $\frac{7}{12}$ **D.** $\frac{7}{60}$

14. Write $\frac{3}{4}$, $\frac{15}{8}$, $1\frac{2}{3}$, $\frac{13}{7}$, $\frac{2}{3}$, $1\frac{1}{5}$ in order from least to greatest.

A. $\frac{2}{3}$, $\frac{3}{4}$, $1\frac{1}{5}$, $1\frac{2}{3}$, $\frac{13}{7}$, $\frac{15}{8}$

B. $\frac{2}{3}$, $\frac{3}{4}$, $1\frac{1}{5}$, $\frac{13}{7}$, $1\frac{2}{3}$, $\frac{15}{8}$

C. $\frac{2}{3}$, $\frac{3}{4}$, $\frac{13}{7}$, $1\frac{1}{5}$, $1\frac{2}{3}$, $\frac{15}{8}$

D. $\frac{2}{3}$, $\frac{3}{4}$, $1\frac{1}{5}$, $\frac{15}{8}$, $\frac{13}{7}$, $1\frac{2}{3}$

15. Write 0.375 as a fraction in simplest form.

A. $\frac{2}{5}$ **B.** $\frac{37}{100}$

C. $\frac{3}{8}$ **D.** $\frac{15}{200}$

16. Add $\frac{2}{3}$ + $\frac{2}{5}$ + $\frac{1}{8}$. Write in simplest form.

A. $1\frac{23}{120}$ **B.** $\frac{123}{120}$

C. $\frac{72}{60}$ **D.** $1\frac{6}{5}$

17. Your mom says you and your 3 friends can have half the pie on the counter. What portion of the pie do each of you get if the portions are all equal?

A. $\frac{1}{3}$ pie   **B.** $\frac{1}{8}$ pie

C. $\frac{1}{6}$ pie   **D.** $\frac{1}{4}$ pie

18. Divide $4\frac{3}{4}$ ÷ $\frac{1}{4}$. Write in simplest form.

A. $\frac{19}{16}$ **B.** $16\frac{3}{16}$

C. $4\frac{1}{4}$ **D.** 19

19. Subtract.   6 lb 4 oz
                  − 2 lb 10 oz

A. 4 lb 4 oz   **B.** 3 lb 4 oz

C. 3 lb 10 oz   **D.** 3 lb 6 oz

20. An airplane leaves Dime Box and flies north 100 mi, 50 mi west, 20 mi south, 100 mi east, and then 80 mi south. How many miles from Dime Box is the plane?

A. 20 mi south   **B.** 50 mi east

C. 50 mi west   **D.** 0 mi

Chapter 9 Cumulative Review

Choose the best answer. Circle A, B, C, or D.

1. Which expression is true?

 A. $13 + 8 \div 2 \times (3 - 1) = 24$

 B. $(13 + 8) \div 2 \times (3 - 1) = 24$

 C. $13 + (8 \div 2) \times (3 - 1) = 24$

 D. $13 + 8 \div 2 \times 3 - 1 = 24$

2. Fill in the missing numbers.
  $8 \times (14 + \blacksquare) = (8 \times \blacksquare) + (\blacksquare \times 3)$

 A. 8, 14, 3   **B.** 3, 14, 8

 C. 14, 8, 3   **D.** 3, 8, 14

3. Use mental math to find the product 0.034×100.

 A. 0.34   **B.** 3.4

 C. 34.0   **D.** 340

4. Use mental math to find the quotient $14.35 \div 0.7$.

 A. 0.205   **B.** 2.05

 C. 20.5   **D.** 2,050

5. Which is the prime factorization tree of 270?

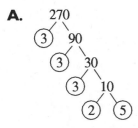

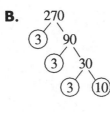

6. Find the GCF of 60 and 96.

 A. 2   **B.** 6

 C. 12   **D.** 32

7. Which fraction is *not* an equivalent fraction to $\frac{6}{9}$?

 A. $\frac{9}{12}$ **B.** $\frac{4}{6}$

 C. $\frac{2}{3}$ **D.** $\frac{12}{18}$

8. Write $\frac{17}{5}$ as a mixed number in simplest form.

 A. $2\frac{2}{5}$ **B.** $3\frac{2}{5}$

 C. $1\frac{7}{5}$ **D.** $3\frac{3}{5}$

9. Write $0.\overline{5}$ as a fraction in simplest form.

 A. $\frac{5}{10}$ **B.** $\frac{55}{100}$

 C. $\frac{5}{9}$ **D.** $\frac{5}{7}$

10. Find the sum. Write the answer in simplest form.
  $\frac{2}{4} + \frac{1}{5} + \frac{1}{6}$

 A. $\frac{27}{30}$ **B.** $\frac{50}{60}$

 C. $\frac{17}{18}$ **D.** $\frac{13}{15}$

11. Find the difference. $11\frac{1}{3} - 8\frac{1}{2}$

 A. $3\frac{5}{6}$ **B.** $3\frac{1}{3}$

 C. $2\frac{1}{6}$ **D.** $2\frac{5}{6}$

12. Jason has $4\frac{3}{8}$ yd of fabric. How many bandanas can he make if each one requires $\frac{5}{8}$ yd of fabric?

 A. 6 bandanas   **B.** 7 bandanas

 C. $5\frac{1}{2}$ bandanas   **D.** $6\frac{1}{5}$ bandanas

Chapter 9 Cumulative Review *(continued)*

13. Find the total area of the two rectangles shown. Write the answer in simplest form.

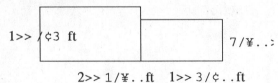

2>> 1/¥..ft   1>> 3/¢..ft

A. $3\frac{5}{8}$ ft^2

B. $5\frac{1}{4}$ ft^2

C. $2\frac{3}{4}$ ft^2

D. $4\frac{2}{3}$ ft^2

14. Add. Write the answer in simplest form.　12 gal 3 qt
　　　+ 11 gal 2 qt

A. 24 gal 1 qt

B. 25 gal

C. 23 gal 1 qt

D. 23 gal 7 qt

15. To qualify for a typing job, Karen needs to type 95 words per min. She timed herself at 450 words for 5 min. What is her rate in comparison to the required rate?

A. She types 5 words per min faster.

B. She types exactly the required rate.

C. She types 5 words per min too slow.

D. She types 15 words per min too slow.

16. Find the value of y in $\frac{33}{y} = \frac{22}{8}$.

A. 6

B. $7\frac{1}{2}$

C. 9

D. 12

17. On a blueprint, you measure the width of a door to be $\frac{3}{4}$ in. The scale on the map is $\frac{1}{4}$ in. : 12 in. What is the actual width of the door?

A. 3 ft

B. 30 in.

C. 2 ft

D. 32 in.

18. Write 44 pens out of 200 pens as a percent, a fraction in simplest form, and a decimal.

A. 44%, $\frac{22}{100}$, 0.22

B. 33%, $\frac{33}{100}$, 0.33

C. 22%, $\frac{11}{50}$, 0.22

D. 22%, $\frac{22}{100}$, 0.2

19. The cost of dinner for you and three of your friends is $48.24. You decide to leave a 17% tip for excellent service. How much of the tip do each of you have to pay to the nearest cent?

A. $2.05

B. $3.00

C. $2.10

D. $8.20

20. The school theater sold 55 tickets to the class play. Adult tickets are $5.00 and children's tickets are $3.50. If a total of 55 tickets are sold for $245.00, how many of each kind were sold?

A. adult: 30; children's: 25

B. adult: 20; children's: 35

C. adult: 27; children's: 28

D. adult: 35; children's: 20

Chapter 10 Cumulative Review

Choose the best answer. Circle A, B, C, or D.

1. What are the next three numbers in this pattern? 2, 8, 14, 20, . . .
   - **A.** 26, 32, 38
   - **B.** 30, 44, 56
   - **C.** 26, 38, 48
   - **D.** 31, 37, 44

2. Use mental math to evaluate $4y + 5$ for $y = 6$.
   - **A.** 24
   - **B.** 29
   - **C.** 30
   - **D.** 6

3. Which variable expression represents this word phrase?
   Fifteen less than twice a number
   - **A.** $x - 2(15)$
   - **B.** $15 - 2x$
   - **C.** $15x - 2$
   - **D.** $2x - 15$

4. Which of the following is a solution to the equation $9 - x = 7$?
   - **A.** 0
   - **B.** 2
   - **C.** 4
   - **D.** 5

5. Solve $3n = 30 + 3$.
   - **A.** 3
   - **B.** 6
   - **C.** 11
   - **D.** 10

6. Add $\frac{3}{14} + \frac{4}{14}$. Write the answer in simplest form.
   - **A.** $\frac{3}{8}$
   - **B.** $\frac{7}{28}$
   - **C.** $\frac{1}{14}$
   - **D.** $\frac{1}{2}$

7. Subtract $1\frac{5}{6} - \frac{23}{14}$. Write the answer in simplest form.
   - **A.** $1\frac{4}{21}$
   - **B.** $\frac{4}{21}$
   - **C.** $\frac{27}{42}$
   - **D.** $\frac{9}{14}$

8. Find the product $1\frac{2}{3} \times 3\frac{1}{4}$.
   - **A.** 5
   - **B.** $3\frac{2}{12}$
   - **C.** $3\frac{2}{9}$
   - **D.** $5\frac{5}{12}$

9. How many pairs of shorts, each requiring $\frac{3}{4}$ yd of fabric, can you make from $6\frac{3}{4}$ yd of fabric?
   - **A.** 9 pairs
   - **B.** 8 pairs
   - **C.** 7 pairs
   - **D.** 10 pairs

10. A recipe calls for 12 oz of milk. How many cups of milk do you need?
    - **A.** 1 c
    - **B.** $1\frac{1}{2}$ c
    - **C.** $1\frac{3}{4}$ c
    - **D.** $2\frac{1}{4}$ c

11. The ratio of 16 pears to 8 apples is *not* the same as
    - **A.** 8 to 4
    - **B.** $2 : 1$
    - **C.** $\frac{2}{1}$
    - **D.** $\frac{1}{2}$

12. Find the value of the variable that makes the ratios equal in $\frac{10}{x} = \frac{15}{24}$.
    - **A.** 16
    - **B.** 36
    - **C.** 12
    - **D.** 18

Course 1 • Chapter 10

Chapter 10 Cumulative Review (continued)

13. Alyssa has 2 quarters, 1 nickel, and 3 pennies. What percent of a dollar does she have?

 A. 0.58% **B.** 5.8%

 C. 58% **D.** 42%

14. A winter coat is on sale for 80% of the original price of $55.89. Estimate the sale price of the coat to the nearest dollar.

 A. $45 **B.** $48

 C. $40 **D.** $47

15. Use the circle graph below. How many hours of the day are spent doing things other than sleeping and working?

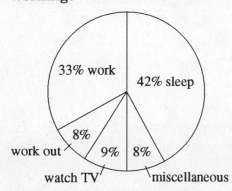

 A. 4 h **B.** 6 h

 C. 8 h **D.** 10 h

16. A bag contains 16 marbles: 3 red, 5 green, 4 blue, 3 yellow, and 1 clear. Find Probability(green) as a fraction, decimal, and percent.

 A. $\frac{11}{16}$, 0.6875, 68.75%

 B. $\frac{5}{16}$, 0.3125, 31.25%

 C. $\frac{1}{4}$, 0.25, 25%

 D. $\frac{5}{16}$, 3.125, 31.25%

17. For dinner the restaurant's menu lists 3 meats, 2 potatoes, 2 salads, and 3 desserts. How many different combinations of one meat, potato, salad, and dessert are there?

 A. 12 combinations

 B. 18 combinations

 C. 36 combinations

 D. 45 combinations

18. How many different ways can you arrange the letters in the word MATH?

 A. 6 ways **B.** 54 ways

 C. 24 ways **D.** 30 ways

19. There are 300 color pegs in a bag. You take out 35 pegs. You find that 15 are white, 6 are green, and the rest are blue. What is *not* a prediction about the rest of the pegs in the bag?

 A. The rest of the pegs are white or blue.

 B. There are about the same number of blue as white pegs.

 C. There are about half the number of green pegs as blue.

 D. There are about twice as many white pegs as green ones.

20. Jason was dog-sitting and took the dog for a walk. He went 6 blocks west, 3 blocks south, 2 blocks east, and 1 block north. How far was he from his starting position?

 A. 1 block east and 3 blocks south

 B. 3 blocks south and 2 blocks west

 C. 2 blocks south and 4 blocks west

 D. 3 blocks west

Chapter 11 Cumulative Review

Choose the best answer. Circle A, B, C, or D.

1. What is the area of the triangle shown?

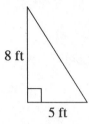

8 ft

5 ft

    A. 13 ft^2 **B.** 20 ft^2

    C. 30 ft^2 **D.** 40 ft^2

2. What is the circumference of a circle with a diameter of 3.2 m? Use 3.14 for π.

    A. 10.048 m   **B.** 3.14 m

    C. 3.2 m   **D.** 6.28 m

3. Find the area of the shaded region. Use 3.14 for π.

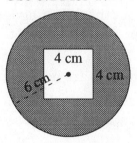

4 cm

6 cm   4 cm

    A. 113.04 cm^2 **B.** 16 cm^2

    C. 97.04 cm^2 **D.** 129.04 cm^2

4. How many faces does a square prism have?

    A. 2 faces   **B.** 4 faces

    C. 6 faces   **D.** 8 faces

5. Find the surface area of the rectangular prism shown.

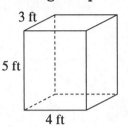

3 ft

5 ft

4 ft

    A. 24 ft^2 **B.** 40 ft^2

    C. 70 ft^2 **D.** 94 ft^2

6. The bicyclist rode 3 mi in 20 min. Find the unit rate in mi/h.

    A. 6 mi/h   **B.** 1 mi/h

    C. 9 mi/h   **D.** 1.5 mi/h

7. Triangles *ABC* and *XYZ* are similar. Which of the following is true?

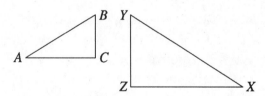

    A. $\dfrac{AB}{BC} = \dfrac{XY}{XZ}$ **B.** $\dfrac{AB}{XY} = \dfrac{BC}{YZ}$

    C. $\dfrac{BC}{YZ} = \dfrac{AC}{YZ}$ **D.** $\dfrac{BC}{YZ} = \dfrac{XZ}{AC}$

8. The distance you need to travel measures 4 in. on the map. The actual trip is 112 mi. What is the scale on the map?

    A. 1 in. : 4 mi

    B. 1 in. : 16 mi

    C. 1 in. : 22 mi

    D. 1 in. : 28 mi

Chapter 11 Cumulative Review *(continued)*

9. What is $\frac{2}{5}$ as a decimal and as a percent?

   A. 0.4, 40%　　　**B.** 0.2, 20%

   C. 0.4, 4%　　　**D.** 0.5, 50%

10. Find 44% of 95.

    A. 38　　　　**B.** 41.8

    C. 4,180　　　**D.** 4.18

11. A bag contains 6 red marbles, 10 black marbles, 1 blue marble, and 17 yellow marbles. Find Probability (choosing red).

    A. $\frac{3}{17}$　　　　**B.** $\frac{14}{17}$

    C. $\frac{1}{34}$　　　　**D.** $\frac{2}{15}$

12. What is the probability of tossing a number cube 3 times and getting a 6 on each toss?

    A. $\frac{1}{216}$　　　**B.** $\frac{1}{6}$

    C. $\frac{1}{36}$　　　　**D.** $\frac{1}{60}$

13. A game has 6 pegs and 6 rings of different sizes. How many ways can you arrange the rings on the pegs with only one ring on each peg?

    A. 56　　　　**B.** 120

    C. 720　　　　**D.** 360

14. Sharran gets her nails done every 5 days and Jessie gets hers done every 4 days. Melissa gets hers done every 8 days. All three got their nails done today. In how many days will all three of them get their nails done on the same day?

    A. 24 days　　　**B.** 25 days

    C. 32 days　　　**D.** 40 days

15. Add $-6 + 3 + (-2)$.

    A. -3　　　　**B.** 5

    C. -5　　　　**D.** -11

16. Subtract $-113 - (-344)$.

    A. 457　　　　**B.** -231

    C. -457　　　**D.** 231

17. In which quadrant is the point with coordinates $(-35, 200)$?

    A. I　　　　**B.** II

    C. III　　　**D.** IV

18. A point with coordinates $(-3, 3)$ is reflected across the x-axis. The point is then translated to the right 2 units and down 3 units. The new coordinates of the point are

    A. $(-3, -3)$　　　**B.** $(-1, -3)$

    C. $(-1, -6)$　　　**D.** $(-6, 0)$

19. A box contains 500 solid objects. A random sample of 55 objects yields 16 pyramids, 10 cubes, 21 cones, and 8 spheres. Which of the following is *not* a prediction about the objects in the box?

    A. Most of the objects are not spheres.

    B. Most of the objects are green.

    C. Most of the objects are either cones or pyramids.

    D. There are no cubes left in the box.

End of Year Self-Assessment Survey

Directions: Answer each question as honestly as possible.

1. Looking at what you have learned is a good way to end the year. Here is a list of skills you have studied in math this year. Check each skill you have learned.

   - [ ] find averages
   - [ ] make bar and line graphs
   - [ ] measure angles
   - [ ] recognize triangles and polygons
   - [ ] find similar figures
   - [ ] write decimals
   - [ ] add decimals
   - [ ] subtract decimals
   - [ ] multiply decimals
   - [ ] divide decimals
   - [ ] find number patterns
   - [ ] write equations
   - [ ] find perimeter and area of polygons
   - [ ] find circumference and area of circles

   - [ ] find common factors
   - [ ] compare fractions
   - [ ] add fractions
   - [ ] subtract fractions
   - [ ] multiply fractions
   - [ ] divide fractions
   - [ ] use ratios
   - [ ] use percents
   - [ ] make circle graphs
   - [ ] make a tree diagram
   - [ ] make predictions
   - [ ] use integers
   - [ ] make coordinate graphs
   - [ ] solve word problems

2. Which skills were fairly easy to learn?

   _____

   _____

   _____

3. Which skills were fun to learn?

   _____

   _____

   _____

4. Which skills did you have to work the hardest to learn?

   _____

   _____

   _____

5. Which skills would you like to learn more about?

   _____

   _____

   _____

Course 1

End of Year Self-Assessment Survey (continued)

6. In math this year, you used certain materials and different methods to help you learn. Check each item that helped you learn more in math.

☐ algebra tiles   ☐ protractor

☐ geoboards   ☐ math journal

☐ fraction bars   ☐ compass and straightedge

☐ calculator   ☐ investigations and projects

☐ pattern blocks   ☐ spreadsheets on the computer

☐ decimal squares   ☐ geometry on the computer

☐ data files   ☐ self-assessment surveys

7. **a.** This year you learned more about using strategies to solve problems. Check each strategy you have learned to use.

_____ make a list   _____ solve a simpler problem

_____ draw a diagram   _____ simulate a problem

_____ guess and test   _____ solve by graphing

_____ look for a pattern   _____ work backward

_____ make a model   _____ write equations

b. Which strategies do you like best?

_____

_____

c. What did you do when you had trouble solving a problem?

_____

_____

8. What was your goal in math this year? Did you reach it?

_____

_____

9. Compared to the beginning of the year, do you like math *more*, *less*, or *about the same*?

_____

_____

10. Of all the things you did in math this year, what are you the most proud of?

_____

_____